KEEP HOPE ALIVE

Memoirs of Khaled M. Diab Imaginatively Retold

Eileen Fleming

Bloomington, IN   authorHOUSE®   Milton Keynes, UK

AuthorHouse™
1663 Liberty Drive, Suite 200
Bloomington, IN 47403
www.authorhouse.com
Phone: 1-800-839-8640

AuthorHouse™ UK Ltd.
500 Avebury Boulevard
Central Milton Keynes, MK9 2BE
www.authorhouse.co.uk
Phone: 08001974150

First published by AuthorHouse 7/27/2006

ISBN: 1-4259-5355-7 (sc)

Library of Congress Control Number: 2006906776

Printed in the United States of America
Bloomington, Indiana

This book is printed on acid-free paper.

The Beatles: The Word

Bob Dylan: The Groom's Still Waiting at the Altar,

Steve Earle: The Revolution Starts Now

David Rovics: They're Building a Wall

U2: BAD

U2: "Love and Peace or Else"

Sabeel Statements and Articles: http://www.sabeel.org

This book is dedicated to the life of Mary Diab and to my cousin Nick Falcone who entered into rest from ALS on April 8, 2005.

I am grateful for many people who made my journey and this book possible, especially my husband John, Dr. Diab, Bill Bauer, Louise Franklin Sheehy, Faith Libbe, G + G and family, and all who have and who will provide and plant olive trees for peace in the land we call holy.

100% of all proceeds to the author will go to the non-profit, non-political Olive Trees Foundation for Peace/OTFFP in Orlando, Florida (www.olivetreesfoundation.org).

The OTFFP efforts are connected to the YWCA in Bethlehem and the YMCA (www.ej-ymca.org) in Jerusalem's Keep Hope Alive Olive Tree Campaign. Our dream is to blanket Gaza with a million fruit-bearing trees and irrigation supplies. Our hope is to change hearts and minds by resisting evil with good and to honor The Divine.

CONTENTS

FOREWORD

by Dr. Khaled Diab

THIS BOOK SHARES SOME of my personal struggles, tribulations, and achievements after October 28, 1948, when I was classified as a Palestinian Refugee. The book describes some of the people I have known and loved deeply. These are my memoirs, but this book also contains characters born from the imagination of the author, Mrs. Eileen Fleming.

This story is about hope and vision, harmony and peace. It is about loving each other and helping those in need. It is about creating a better world with hope for a better future for our children and theirs.

My relationships with Christians, Jews, and Muslims who treat each other with respect have filled me with hope for our collective future. By praying together, working as partners, and sharing our pain, we have found peace and joy. We found hope when we chose to quit trying to find justice through the contorted prism of *who is to blame*.

Peace will come when people of goodwill act to create the three basic elements of peace. These elements are Possibilities, Reconciliation and Opportunity. These elements form the Olive Trees Foundation's PRO plan. Twenty-five trees will provide the opportunity to sustain the average Palestinian family of five. That would change hearts and minds and then reconciliation will be possible between the children of Father Abraham.

Beginning in 2003, the OTFFP has created children's parks in the West Bank and provided the funds for over 30,000 olive trees, which are now rooted in Israel and Palestine.

Dr. Khaled M. Diab
Founder and President, Olive Trees Foundation for Peace
http://www.olivetreesfoundation.org

INTRODUCTION

It has been said that all stories are true, and some actually happened. *Keep Hope Alive* is both and more. This tale is a fictionalized retelling of the memoirs of a refugee who realized the American dream. This story is also a historical chronology of many of the events of the days from 1948 on, with connections to antiquity, and hope for the future.

Keep Hope Alive is also my journey told through the fictional characters of Riad, Jack Hunt, Dr. Jake and Terese Hunter. Born in Greenwich Village in 1954 I came of age in Levittown, Long Island during the 1960s: a grandchild of immigrants--Russian Orthodox, Polish Jew, and Irish Catholic.

Keep Hope Alive is for every American who experienced 9/11 and have not been satisfied with easy answers. *Keep Hope Alive* also provides an opportunity for the reader to literally extend the olive branch of reconciliation, for all proceeds to the author will go directly to plant olive trees in Israel Palestine.

While some of the characters within these pages are fictional everything they say is true. And almost everything actually happened.

Eileen Fleming
June 25, 2006

Much more on WAWA:
http://www.wearewideawake.org

Chapter 1:

The Morning After April 4, 1968

Mary woke at dawn and re-entered the living room for the first time since she had said goodnight the night before. She was not surprised to see Khaled sprawled out in his recliner or Riad at peace on the sofa. But she was dismayed to see Art curled in fetal position on the black and white checkered tile at the front door.

She gently stepped over him into the red and white kitchen as the morning sun broke through the garden window. The sun illuminated the cherry-blonde slab stump of an ancient olive tree that had been hewn into a kitchen table and received as a wedding gift from family and friends, who lived in Khaled's hometown, the village of Majd Al Krum, in Upper Galilee. Even on the most frigid morning, Mary felt warmed by the high-gloss patina of the tabletop, but held more dear the signatures and marks from the entire town etched underneath.

Mary silently performed the morning ritual of brewing the first of many pots of Turkish coffee for the day, gratefully inhaled the piquant aroma, and then quickly exited up the back staircase to the bedrooms to wake her daughter for school. When Mary returned to her kitchen after escorting Ahmeena to her third grade classroom, she was not surprised to find Khaled and Riad at the table, downing a second pot of the Turkish brew.

"Please, Mary, don't say a word. I drank too much, and now I am paying the price."

"Khaled, the pain in your face brings me to tears; you are clearly suffering. I will not add to your misery. But you, Riad--you look buoyant. What's your secret?"

Riad chuckled. "Tolerance."

Mary marveled at how his gleaming pate radiated the sun's reflection through the garden window that showcased a pendulous purple wisteria and bird bath, where blue jays had immediately gathered to eat the seed she had just put out.

At that moment, Art stumbled into the room, banging his shoulder against the wall and hip into the butcher-block counter. "Crap. Sylvia is going to fry me; I thought I'd be back at her sister's by noon. But until I get a few pots of coffee and a pack of cigarettes in me, I'll never be any good. That bad news about Martin Luther King, Jr., hit us all like a left to the liver! I thought last night would be only good reminiscing, but reality intruded. Thanks, Mary." He nodded and gratefully downed the pungent brew that Mary had just set before him.

"So, who wants breakfast?"

"Just toast, Mary, my love," Khaled whimpered weakly.

"Same for me." Riad beamed, and Mary thought how grateful she was to know him.

Art whispered, "Have you any Mylanta, Mary?"

Mary suppressed a smile as she turned to retrieve it, when the unmistakable knock of Ahmad was heard. Knock, knock, knock, knock!

"*Namaste!*" Ahmad bellowed as he entered the front door, reminding her of a Cheshire cat without any guile.

Riad replied, with a beatific smile, "The God in me salutes the God in you, too."

"Art and Khaled, look what I found in the gutter." Ahmad nudged a redheaded muscular youth forward as hard as he could.

"Why, Jack Hunt, I haven't seen you in weeks; come in, dear." Mary was always happy to see any of the eleven Hunt children who lived next door.

Khaled stood to welcome his neighbor and asked, "Jack, why aren't you in class this morning?"

"Well, I didn't know until I showed up that poli-sci and humanities were canceled. Both professors are heading to King's funeral. They marched with him first in 1964. I am free until three, when I have football practice. I was just getting out of the car and hoping to catch up on some sleep, when Ahmad accosted me and dragged me in here."

Riad stood with his palms together and slightly bowed. "Welcome, Jack. I'm Riad, and the poor fellow to my right is Art."

"Oh man, Art, you look like shit! I hope it's not contagious."

"Shut up and sit," Art growled.

"Ahmad, we expected you for dinner last night. I made your favorite—roasted lamb."

"Oh, yes, sorry. After I left Khaled's going-away party at Westinghouse, I worked through the night. In fact, I have not eaten since the goodbye brunch yesterday; I could use some lamb right now."

Mary turned swiftly and began emptying the refrigerator. While Art moaned, she asked, "Please, Ahmad, I have not heard a word about the going-away party; fill me in."

Ahmad grinned and nodded. "Well, the best part was at the very end, when Khaled stood at the microphone and spoke with tears in his eyes to the two hundred people who had gathered to say goodbye. He held us spellbound with his words: 'My dear friends, I am overwhelmed by this turnout. I have been blessed. I will miss you all very much. Thank you for the kind words, the gifts, the memories, and all your good work. I also want to leave a remembrance with one of you.'

"And it was I, Ahmad, who held the fish bowl filled with everyone's signatures that Khaled reached his hand into and fished out the paper scrap, unfolded it, and called out, 'Oh, Bubbles McGrath! You have won. Come up here and receive your gift!' Now, Bubbles is a short, plump blonde, who jumped up like a toad and screamed, 'Oh my gosh! I have never won anything!' She literally bounced her way to where Khaled and I stood, but I quickly got out of the way, as the man of the hour held out a festively wrapped box like a shield to protect himself from the force of the rushing Bubbles McGrath. She flung her arms around Khaled and kissed him on the mouth, then blurted out, 'Oh, thank you, Khaled, I am so excited!' It was incredible, how she tore the box open like a child at Christmas, and when her face beheld the treasure inside, her lower lip quivered, and she quietly whispered, 'Thanks.' Then she held out the gunmetal gray snow shovel, and the room roared!"

Mary had noticed Jack was oblivious to Ahmad's tale. As he stared out the garden window, she knew he was worried about his sister Bonnie, a WAC nurse in Vietnam, and his brother Kevin, who was in the Navy. While the men were still chuckling over Ahmad's tale, Jack startled them all as his words rushed out. "My professor told me that he marched with King because, even though he himself was an atheist, he felt comfortable with the diversity of people of faith and none in particular who had come together as a community. He said King had a power to make you believe you were connected to every other person in the crowd like a sister or a brother."

A heavy, pregnant silence filled the room, and Mary held her breath until Jack turned toward her, his eyes like blazing emeralds, and with a sardonic smile, remarked, "Being stuck in the middle of ten others, I have no desire for any more sisters or bothers." Then, with a sigh deeper than words and overcast eyes, he gently spoke. "I will be sorry when you Diabs depart for sunny Florida. I always appreciated you letting me use your library, Dr. D."

Mary turned as her tears fell, and Khaled mumbled, as he choked back his own, "We will all miss you, too, Jack, but we have a few weeks left before we will part. Let's have some coffee now!"

Riad beckoned Jack to sit at his right side, but Jack shook his head. "Ah, that's ok. Really, I have got to go. Practice is at three o'clock, and I only came back home to get some sleep."

Khaled implored, "Jack, please, sit and visit. Mary, where is his coffee? Besides, Riad has some fantastic tale we never got to hear last night, and now is the time. Riad, the floor is yours."

Jack remained unmoved as Riad queried, "Have you heard the tale of the Bedouin named Mohammed Ali? No? How about the Nag´ Hammâdi library? Hmmm, do you know I am a master of ancient civilizations, and I speak Greek and Hebrew fluently? You are not impressed; I can see. How about, have you heard of UNESCO?"

Jack barely suppressed a smirk as he sat down in one of the seven eclectic chairs that hugged the sides of the enormous olivewood table and murmured, "United Nation Educational Scientific and Cultural Organization."

"Correct, but I'll get to that later. My story dates back to antiquity. But I will begin in 1945, in Egypt, in the land just above the bend of the Nile, north of the Valley of the Kings, across the river from the city of Nag´ Hammâdi, near the hamlet of al-Qasr, under a cliff called Jabal al-Tarif. An Egyptian Bedouin named Mohammed Ali was out gathering sabakh, a nitrate-rich fertilizer for the crops that he grew in the small hamlet of al-Qasr. He was aghast to stumble upon a skeleton as he dug, and bewildered when he uncovered a two-foot high earthenware jar. A bowl had been placed over the top, and it was sealed with bitumen. At first, the Bedouin thought an evil genie was within, but when he shook the heavy jar, he heard things moving and thought it might be gold. He smashed the jar open and out fluttered pieces of gold particles that he tried to catch, but they disappeared. When he peered into the jar, he was dismayed only to find twelve leather-bound books. Mohammed Ali was illiterate, so he placed no great value on books, but was confident he could sell them and make something for his troubles. So he carried the jar filled with books back to the homestead.

"He also happened to be a fugitive from the law, for he had wielded the weapon that spilled the blood of a patriarch during a violent incident in a generation-long family feud, not so very long before. After a few days of mulling over possibilities, he decided to give his find to the local Coptic priest for safekeeping. He feared the authorities soon would be lurking about to confiscate his possession before he could receive any money for it.

"His mother had been ripping out pages to keep the home fire going, and I often wonder what ancient treasures she burned. Who knows what was lost. Anyway, the priest passed it on to his brother-in-law, a traveling tutor, who brought the books to the Coptic museum in Cairo on October 4, 1946.

"I happened to be the assistant to the director of the antiquities department at that time, and our department was immediately summoned to inspect them. What we found were ancient compositions, written in Coptic that had been translated from ancient Greek. The volumes were leather-bound pages of papyrus, and no doubt the gold dust that Mohammed Ali witnessed was from papyrus fragments that had broken off. For the past twenty years, under the leadership of UNESCO, Egypt, and the American scholar James Robinson, these anthologies and collections of texts with titles like the Gospel of Thomas and the Gospel of Mary Magdalene have been translated."

Jack's eyes glinted as he quietly spoke. "So?"

"Well, I believe when this knowledge has been disseminated by seekers of God, it will prove to be a revolutionary find. You see, the texts date back to the early days of Christianity. The most likely source for these books was the Pachomius Monastery, which thrived for centuries just three miles from the burial site. I believe a monk buried these books in the wilderness under the cliff of Jabl al-Tarif for safe-keeping."

"But why would a monk hide some books? What for?" Jack sipped his coffee as he kept his eyes riveted on Riad.

"Well Jack, two thousand years ago, there were many different understandings of Jesus among Christians. Now, thanks to the treasures of Nag' Hammâdi, we know how rich and diverse those understandings were. These texts had been deemed heretical by those who were gaining power through the political arena. Surely you know about Emperor Constantine?"

"Of course, he lived in the fourth century, didn't he? Wasn't he a pagan warrior who became the first Christian ruler, but waited until he was on his deathbed before being baptized?"

"Yes, and the most decisive event in the history of Christendom occurred when Emperor Constantine accepted the Christian faith, for those who had once been persecuted were now protected by an earthly king. Both a patriarchal monarchical state and church were formed at the same time. Power struggles and debates were common among the early Christians. Individual churches determined which texts were read, and they all had their favorites. Constantine sought to unite his empire, and uniting the church was a savvy political move. He announced he would pay for fifty illuminated copies of scripture to be bound, and thus the biblical canon was established and sealed. There was fierce debate among the bishops about what should be included and what left out.

"The proto-orthodox, who had now become the dominant voice, determined what was heretical for everyone. The proto-orthodox demanded much-loved scripture to be burned, usually because it did not fit their understanding of God. No doubt, what was found at Nag' Hammâdi is thanks to an unknown monk who lived a few miles away in the Pachomius Monastery. If the authorities had found out about him, these texts and that monk would both have been burned!"

"But why were the books deemed heretical? Why were they suppressed? What was the establishment afraid of?" Jack's eyes remained riveted on Riad.

"Well Jack, many of these texts were considered Gnostic. Gnosis is defined as knowledge discerned institutively. Gnostic texts offer deep mystery that is discerned via intuition, not rational thought. This is not the way of fundamentalists. A Gnostic is open to receiving intuitive knowledge of deep spiritual truth. For students of the New Testament, this is a much greater find than the Dead Sea Scrolls. Forty of the texts had previously been unknown to modern scholars. Thirty-five scholars have been working diligently on these translations, and we all agree that the bound books themselves date back to the fourth century and were written in Coptic translated from Greek and Aramaic. The Gospel of Thomas is a collection of the sayings of Jesus, words of wisdom, proverbs, parables, and some very confounding mysteries. About 35 of the 114 sayings have no counterpart in the New Testament, while at least 20 are almost identical, and 54 have similarities. Many scholars concur that the sayings were originally written in Syriac, a dialect of Aramaic, the language of Jesus and his followers. It is very possible the sayings are closer to the words Jesus actually spoke than what is found in the canonical gospels."

"I am still not clear about why there was so much censorship. If the people were talking about Jesus and what he said, that seems better than not talking about him at all."

"Agreed, and two thousand years ago, there was lively debate about who Jesus was, and why he came. Jack, you do understand that history is always written by the winners, right?"

"Of course. And now, I suppose you will tell me all about the losers?"

"Well, the proto-orthodox, who were the majority, considered these texts anathema. Texts were deemed heretical for many reasons, and usually it was because they did not fit neatly into the evolving dogma. Gnostic texts offer us mystery, not answers. For centuries, all we had to reconstruct Gnostic beliefs were the hostile accounts against them given by Irenaus, Tertullian, Hippolytus, Epiphanius, and other church fathers who disagreed with the Gnostic understanding."

"Yeah, well, I don't do church anymore, but my sister Maureen is a nun, and my brother Mike is a priest. I wonder what they would think of all this stuff."

"Now Jack, we must be kind to the early church fathers; they were flawed like all of humanity, but they did the best they could. We are all guided by the inner light and by how much light we have opened up to receive. The gifts of Nag' Hammâdi present us with a very diverse Christianity, indeed.

"One of my favorites is the Gospel of Thomas. These pithy sayings of Jesus are meant to be heard and chewed upon. Consider sayings three and five: 'The kingdom is inside you, and it is outside you. When you know yourselves, then you will be known, and you will understand that you are children of the living father,'[1] and 'Know what is in front of your face, and what is hidden will be disclosed to you. For there is nothing hidden that will not be revealed.'"[2]

"Hey, that reminds me of 'seek and you will find,' and 'knock and the door will open.'

"Yes, you see the connection. And in Thomas, sayings ninety-two and ninety-four, Jesus says exactly that. But in saying two, Jesus speaks: 'Let one who seeks not stop seeking until one finds. When one finds, one will be troubled. When one is troubled, one will marvel.'"[3]

Jack interrupted with "Wait, I still do not get what was the big deal. Why did the authorities want these books trashed?"

"Jack, did you know that the Gospel of Mark was written first, in about 70 CE? Then Matthew and Luke followed in 85 CE, and the very different-sounding Gospel of John appeared just before the turn of the first century. The Gospel of Thomas was written down as early as the middle of the first century, and no later than the middle of the second."

Jack interrupted. "You mean it may have been written even before the Gospel of John?"

"Exactly, and that is why I wonder if the author of John was debating many of Jesus' sayings quoted by the author of Thomas. In particular, I was struck by the fact that Matthew 12:31-32, Mark 3:28-29, and Luke 12:10 are nearly identical to Thomas saying forty-four, 'Jesus said, "Whoever blasphemes against the father will be forgiven, and whoever blasphemes against the son will be forgiven, but whoever blasphemes against the Holy Spirit will not be forgiven either on earth or in heaven.'[4] The writer of John completely left this quote from Jesus out. What do you think about that, Jack?"

"Well, it sounds like Jesus is just alright with whatever you think or say about him, but the Holy Spirit--that's God within. It sounds like Jesus is saying it's not so much what we think or say about him, but how we treat one another and ourselves."

"Spoken well!" Ahmad grinned as he continued, "If I may share a moment, there is the Hindu way to God through love, and it is the way Jesus taught. In fact, Christianity is one great brilliantly-lit highway to God! This Hindu discipline is called *bhajti yoga*; it is the path I follow. What is required upon this path is loving God first, with no ulterior motives, not even a desire to be loved back. All day, as I do my work, I do it for God. I am in love with God, and that fills me with a love for all men and all creation. Love God first, and everything else falls into place, I say."

Jack had become excited. "You just made me remember what Mike wrote to me, after he heard Thomas Merton speak at what became his last peace rally, before he was electrocuted in a freak accident and died. My brother was standing next to this nun who accosted Merton after his speech and demanded, 'Why didn't you mention Christ in your speech?' Merton replied, 'What we are asked to do at present is not so much to speak of Christ as to let him live in us, so that people may find him by feeling how he lives in us.'[5] Mike wrote that after overhearing that encounter, he quit giving his parishioners the usual list of prayers to say for penance. He told them not to mention Jesus by name for a week, but instead keep him foremost in their minds and hearts."

Riad beamed. "Jack, your brother is a wise man to think of such a just penance for Christians who may forget the other names for Jesus, like Emmanuel, meaning 'God is with us,' and the Prince of Peace. And Martin Luther King, Jr., walked in his footsteps; I hope we never forget his message of justice and equality for all humanity."

Khaled met Art's eyes and gently spoke. "You know, Martin Luther King is foremost the voice for the Negro, but he also speaks for all who seek justice. He said, 'we have come to this hallowed spot to remind America of the fierce urgency of now. Now is the time for justice; now is the time to make real the promises of democracy. Now is the time to lift our nation from injustice to the solid rock of brotherhood.'"[6]

Art stabbed out his cigarette and injected, "Yeah, and do you know what Reverend King said just a few weeks ago? He said, 'Peace for Israel means security, and we stand with all our might to protect its right to exist, its territorial integrity. I see Israel as one of the great outposts of democracy in the world, and a marvelous example of what can be done, how desert land can be transformed into an oasis of brotherhood and democracy. Peace for Israel means security and that security must be a reality.'"[7]

Khaled nearly blubbered, "Reality? The reality is that Israel's democracy does not extend to Palestinians, whose families have lived there for centuries! Martin Luther King also spoke about not 'being satisfied until justice rolls down like waters, and righteousness like a mighty stream.'[8] Reverend King also spoke about his people's great trials, tribulations, and creative suffering. He spoke about injustice, but offered such hope for change, because the American dream is that all men are created equal. This is also the Palestinian dream. Reverend King spoke of his dream, and I, too, have a dream, that underneath the shade of olive trees, the descendants of Abraham will one day sit down at the table of brotherhood."

Art lit another cigarette as he added, "My rabbi always says, 'If we would all just do like Micah told, we'd be alright. Do justice, love mercy, and walk humbly with your God.'"[9]

Khaled erupted. "I wonder if Israeli Prime Minister Levi Eshkol ever read Micah. I read that when he was told by his generals that the IDF was the greatest army since King David, he became ecstatic! I cannot understand why the American government is ignoring the situation in my homeland, when, in 1956, the US demanded Israel withdraw from the Sinai Desert back to the international border after only three months. The Six Day War was a year ago, and no such demands were made. They have turned a blind eye to the destruction of Palestinian towns, and I cannot believe America has not stood up to the Israelis. Not a word of condemnation about the massive building projects in the West Bank, Sinai, Eastern Jerusalem, and the Golan Heights! Not a word that Palestinians are still living in refugee camps, and their homes and olive groves have been plowed over! Why doesn't America demand equally just treatment for Palestinians, too? Yes, yes, yes, America is focused on Vietnam. Now we mourn Martin Luther King in America, and I mourn the lack of justice in my homeland."

Art violently snuffed out his cigarette and boomed, "Look, the situation is untenable. We got nowhere discussing this last night, and you cannot forget what my people, my very family, suffered beyond belief from the Nazis! You cannot compare the two! Then, we must endure the inflammatory rhetoric to 'push the Jews into the sea!' Why, of course we believed another Holocaust was about to happen. How can you blame us after all we have suffered while the world remained mute? Nobody spoke out to protect us when the Nazis were exterminating us in ovens. My God! How can you blame us for attacking first? Anyone would have, if they had suffered as my people have. How can you blame us for attacking first?"

Khaled kindly replied, "Of course, we all deeply regret the atrocities that were inflicted upon the Jewish people. But that pain should not be used as a reason to inflict pain on others."

Riad shook his head, removed his thick-lens, thin wire-rimmed spectacles and rubbed his myopic eyes. "Yes, we all agree there, and must be sensitive to the suffering the Jewish people have endured throughout history. I was in Egypt when the UN forces stationed on the Egyptian-Israeli border left, and what happened next? The Egyptians blockaded the Straits of Tiran and cut off Israeli shipping access to the Port of Eliat. Such infantile behavior from world leaders! It's always about control and keeping power."

Art was agitated. "Yes, Khaled, it is true that just a few weeks after that blockade, Egypt, Syria, Jordan, and Iraq signed a mutual defense agreement designed to facilitate a combined attack on Israel. They want to obliterate Israel! You see, Khaled, Israel had no choice but to attack first!"

Khaled was miserable. "I read that President Johnson was asked to intervene, but I am sad. Vietnam preoccupies this country. I am sad about many things. It was only seven years ago in his farewell address that President Eisenhower warned the American people to beware of the military-industrial complex. He warned us of the danger of becoming dependent on the manufacturing of weapons to stimulate our economy. It was a year ago that Martin Luther King warned us that 'any nation, who, year after year, spends more money on military defense than on programs of social uplift is approaching spiritual death.'[10] What I see going on in the world is that everyone seems to believe that stockpiling weapons will ensure peace and provide many jobs. This is false security, and sows the seeds that war is the way to peace."

Riad rubbed his gleaming dome and looked directly at Art. "The Jewish people have been threatened throughout their entire history. It is understandable they are paranoid. It is justified! But, that does not justify them treating others unjustly. The Israeli nation is surrounded by refugee camps--refugee camps filled with Palestinians who were forced off their land by threat of their own holocaust. Poor leadership on all sides brings us to this place in time. The horrors and injustice of the Holocaust are still fresh in Jewish minds. It should remain fresh within all our minds. We should never forget the injustice of the Holocaust. We should never forget that man's inhumanity to man was able to proliferate because good people did nothing. The nations of the world turned a blind eye to the pain and injustice the Jewish people suffered until too many had died. Now, the Palestinians are being ignored by the world and are fighting back in ways that will not help their cause. Injustice must always be confronted and be withstood by peaceful means. When will this be understood?"

"Get real, Riad. The PLO wants to wipe us out! But God is on our side. After all, we won the war in only seven days! The Arab nations received a left to the liver by Israeli's pre-emptive strike, and now we control the Sinai, Gaza Strip, Suez Canal in Egypt, West Bank, and East Jerusalem in Jordan. Why, now the entire city of Jerusalem is under Israeli control! Surely you see the hand of God in this?"

Khaled was steaming, while Riad gently spoke. "I know you do, Art, but I see a different side. Superior military force, and the fact that Israel was supplied with American intelligence and knew exactly where to strike, won it.

Eighteen thousand Arab soldiers died, and Palestinian refugees continue to be ignored. By her silence, America has legitimized the Israeli victory, and I fear ahead of us will be more injustice, death, and destruction. Last December, George Habash founded the Popular Front for the Liberation of Palestine. It is a terrorist organization inspired by communism. Each side ups the ante with more death and destruction. When will it ever be enough?"

Art sighed deeply and offered, "You are right, Riad; when will it be enough? The Torah teaches that everyone is a part of God and created in the divine image. We can even agree with Jesus that the greatest command is that we love God with our whole hearts, souls, minds, and strength. I suppose, if everyone did that, it would be a perfect world. You know I love you, man, but I have got to hit the road. Sylvia and I are flying back home to Iowa City tonight, but we will definitely see you soon in Orlando."

While Khaled and Mary escorted Art to his car, Jack turned to Riad and asked, "What religion are you?"

Riad smiled cryptically as he sighed, "Child, I am a student of all; my mind is open to the wisdom of every tradition, and I am still exploring. May I ask you, Jack, if you agree that we are all flawed, imperfect beings? Do you believe we all come from the same source, and we will return to that source when this journey is through? Can you entertain the thought that this life just might, in fact, be a dress rehearsal for the next? Do you agree that we all hear the message of the good news, limited by our own spiritual, intellectual, and psychological capacities?"

Jack's eyes had become dazzling emeralds, and Riad laughed from his gut. "Jack, I must be careful with you. It is with patience we are to run the race set before us, but I sense you would like to hear about the stages of the soul, no?"

"Riad, you are some kind of strange, but please, go on."

Riad sweetly intoned, "Ah, Jack, I will not argue with you, and I joyfully share with you that the spiritual journey is fluid, not static. One may pass back and forth through any of the four, and maybe more, stages of the soul in one's journey.[11] Stage one is essentially our infancy in the spiritual life. Like a wild child, a person in this stage reflects the inner chaotic and anti-social, unregenerate soul that is interested only in its own self-satisfaction and ego. Stage one people may claim to love others, but their behavior reflects that they love their own pleasure, money, power, prestige, and security above any other. For stage one people, it really is all about them.

"The good news is that God is already within us, so the vast majority of humanity responds to that inner tug and seeks God, entering stage two. These folks live virtuous lives and do many good works. They also can be rigid, fundamental, and legalistic. They adhere to a higher human authority than themselves for guidance. They submit to institutions, scripture, dogma, ritual, ministers, or gurus. This is the most appropriate stage for older children and most adults. A difference between stages one and two is that a stage one person wouldn't even notice a neighbor in need, while a stage two person has awoken to the fact that we are to be our neighbors' keepers.

"Now, stage three souls have awakened to the realization that one's neighbor is everyone on the planet, and not just those who think and look alike. Stage threes are seekers, doubters, skeptics, and may even become atheists or agnostics. They will study philosophy and other religions, and often become activists for social justice and reform.

"Then there is stage four, which is the way of the mystic. A mystic can be understood as one in love with the divine mystery, and one who is aware of the unity of all creation. They have gone beyond their concepts of God to an intuitive comprehension of the divine in all creation. They are awake to the action of God within themselves and others. Saint Francis, the leper kisser of Assisi, was a mystic--head over heels in love with God, in everyone and all creation. Many thought him nuts, or at least, eccentric. The mystic realizes the connections and unity of all beings, places, situations, past, present, and future. This person has traveled beyond their concept of God, not by personal effort, but in response to the invitation of God.

"Now, Jack, you have a very wild look in your eyes; I hope I have not disturbed you too much. Please, understand that it would be violence upon a soul to rush the work of God. A stage one or two should remain that way until God beckons them on."

Mary and Khaled had returned to the kitchen just as Jack's eyes bored into Riad's, and his voice cracked, "You know, Mr. Riad, I'd like to tell you why I tuned out the institutional church. Up until I was about eight years old, every Sunday morning was spent standing in a glass-encased room that was called, and literally was, the cry room. I would stand at this soundproof glass and watch this show on the other side. My brother Mike was an altar boy. I'd make faces at him, hoping to crack him up, but he never looked my way. Every so often, I'd hear the priest's voice filter through the loudspeaker above my head. But it was all in Latin! There I was, surrounded by squirming kids and uptight adults, engulfed by the sounds of crying and whining, and I truly believed this was church. Once my younger siblings had grown, we got to be in the main room. It was ok.

"But when I turned fifteen in 1963, three things occurred. By Thanksgiving that year, I was overfilled with images of JFK being shot and John-John during that motorcade. I still can't get that little guy in his short coat with his knees exposed out of my head. He saluted as the casket rode by, but nobody knew why it had to be that way. And life as I had known it all changed. But God is good, and three months later, the gloom had gone. For the Beatles appeared on a Sunday night in my living room, and the world as I had known it was never the same. Recently, John Lennon made a comment to a reporter that the Beatles were more popular with my generation than Jesus, and he was right on. My friends and I know every lyric to every Beatles song, but nobody ever quotes Jesus.

"Lennon made me think about my own hypocrisy, and that led me to drop the church. It happened at weekly confession; there I was at the altar, kneeling down, saying the same prayers as always, but this was for the last time. In the middle of the three Our Fathers and ten Hail Marys, it hit me like a light. These words that I uttered never changed anything, and I got up and walked out for the last time. But now, I understand; I'm just a stage one! But, the thing is, you have given me a lot to think about. Maybe I was just born into the wrong faith."

Ahmad smiled even wider and exclaimed, "Jack, a Hindu would advise you to follow the path you have been born into. Seek God in your family tradition. Seek where you have been placed. If, after you truly seek God there, you do not find him, then go seek him wherever he leads. Now, have you heard what Gandhi said about Christianity, Jack? He said that it was a most excellent religion; they should all try it."

"Too bad Gandhi wasn't there during the Crusades! Those barbarians tortured and burned people at the stake! What kind of Christian could rationalize that? So much hypocrisy! I will not give my soul over to another. No institution is going to control me!" Jack announced triumphantly, and then continued, "My best bud Al is a Jew, and we both have tuned out what our elders have offered—too many rules! Besides, I think Christians can be real cowards, or else they were sleeping while Hitler was gaining power. I hate to think it, but maybe it was because they are anti-Semitic?"

Riad interrupted, "I won't comment on that, but in 1965, the Second Vatican Council issued a declaration on the relationship of the church to non-Christian religions, condemning anti-Semitism, and recognizing 'the bond that spiritually ties the people of the New Covenant to Abraham's stock.'[12] Now, I realize nineteen centuries of anti-Semitism and some very unholy behavior will not erase the sins of the fathers, but with this new revelation begins the healing. Hope emerges every time a wrong has been admitted and corrected."

Art had returned unnoticed and had silently stood in the doorway until Riad finished. He softly spoke. "Excuse me. The book Sylvia had been reading to me while we traveled--it's a collection of Einstein's essays. I was driving down your street when a white cat darted in front of me, and I hit the brakes. The book fell on the floor, and that cat went up a tree and sat, and just stared at me with his icy blue eyes. The book fell open to 'The Calling of The Jews.'

I quote: 'This is a time when there seems to be a particular need for men of philosophical persuasion—that is to say, friends of wisdom and truth—to join together...We Jews should be, and remain, the carriers and patrons of spiritual values. But we should also always be aware of the fact that these spiritual values are and always have been the common goal of mankind.'[13] Einstein's advice should be heeded by all men of good will. But it seems to me that we all can claim to do God's will, and yet we all can too easily justify unjust behavior."

The Muslim and the Jew locked eyes, and tears welled up from within them both, then overflowed at the same time. After a time of timelessness, Riad softly spoke. "I offer you Thomas saying forty-eight, and I quote: 'Jesus said, "If two make peace with each other in a single house, they will say to the mountain, 'move from here', and it will be done.'"[14]

Art exhaled smoke as he spoke directly to Khaled. "I just had another memory about how you came to be the owner of a '41 Pontiac with a dent in the side door that--"

"Oh, no, Art, you can't tell that one without me first laying the foundation. I remember it well. Jack, did I tell you that my friend here, Art Pearlman, hired me while I was still in college? Right on the spot, and he never regretted it. Art was the director of the assistant-engineer-in-training program at the John Deere Company, and supervised with an iron hand and warm heart. While still a sophomore at State University of Iowa, I was promoted after four months on the job to be Art's right-hand man. We had become like brothers! Jack, remember when I told you about Gloria breaking my heart? Yes, well, Art watched me brood the entire week after we broke up, and he refused to allow me to keep my broken heart to myself!"

Art grinned and continued, "It was unbearable. I said, 'enough with the stony silence; you look like you are ready to explode. It's been a long, hard week. Let's knock off early and grab a beer. You haven't said a word all week—no jokes, no smiles. Who died? What happened with you?' Oh, how you sighed as you related your tale of woe. I can still hear you whine, 'I have decided I will never get married unless I marry a girl from my own culture. And here in Iowa, I have not met any!' You cried in your beer, and then I suggested you forget about marriage, have some fun, and date some of those beautiful college girls I watched all over town."

"Yes, you made a good point, Art. But college girls only dated college men who owned a car. Not only did I not own a car, I did not even know how to drive. But, I began imagining myself behind the wheel of an automobile and having many dates! So, the next thing I knew, we were on Mallard Avenue, at Jim's Used Car Lot. We were immediately pounced upon by Jim, who demanded, 'What are you looking to spend?' I immediately remembered a traumatic experience with a Syrian rug merchant when I first fled Majd Al Krum in 1948, and I shivered and said, 'Speak with my advisor, Art.' Jim placed his hands upon our backs and led us through the lot, telling us every car was a bargain. We stopped in front of a shiny black sedan with a dent in the passenger-side door, and then Art took over like the master he is."

"Right, I negotiated a sweet deal for that pony, just two hundred dollars, cash! But, Khaled still didn't know how to drive. So I chauffeured him to the public parking lot a few blocks from his boarding house, and had to catch the bus back to the dealership to retrieve my car. That weekend was a nephew's bar mitzvah, but I promised, come Monday after work, I would give Khaled his first driving lesson."

"Ah, I couldn't wait. I could already taste all those dates! I buoyantly walked to the campus library, humming Arabic tunes, and located every book about clutches and cars that I could find. Not until the librarian flicked the lights at eleven at night, did I leave. I carried home a dozen books about cars and spent the rest of the night reading.

"As soon as the dawn broke, I headed to the public parking lot and admired my acquisition. I carried the car keys in my pocket and thought, I don't have to wait for Art; I know what to do. So, I climbed behind the wheel, located the ignition, and inserted the key. The car jumped, and I panicked, until I located the brake, and sat gripping the wheel and praying, 'Please God, don't let me hurt anyone or anything.' For hours, I practiced, until I mastered the clutch and was grateful I only scratched up an old relic that someone had abandoned in the lot. By noon, I was confidently circling the lot and tempted to venture out into the street. I reluctantly paralleled parked, waited until Monday morning, and arrived at work, beaming. 'Art, I have great news. I taught myself to drive; I am skipping lunch today. I am ready to take my driver's license test.'

"Well, we skipped lunch, and sure enough, Khaled scored a hundred percent on the written exam and drove back to work like a pro!"

"Yes, and when I got back to my rooming house, I beeped the horn just once with sheer delight, and the old woman who lived next door stuck her head out the window and began cursing at me. I had feigned ignorance of English at each encounter with her, and by maintaining a stony silence in her presence, I was able to learn every American curse word!

"That fall of 1954, when I returned to classes and resumed my tasks as assistant professor in manufacturing processes, Professor Harding remarked, 'Khaled, now that you have a car, you never get to class on time. You are consistently a few minutes late; what is the matter?' I shrugged and replied, 'It is difficult to find parking.' Professor Harding laughed and said, 'Now you have learned that every good thing has a dark lining.' By the first snowfall of the season, I had been successful in routinely scheduling two dates on every Saturday. I had just dropped Judy back to campus after an afternoon of ice-skating, and was heading to the cleaners to pick up my only suit before an evening out with Debbie. The snow had started a few hours before, and I had never driven upon freezing rain. I almost slid into the Waterloo River before deciding to park that Pontiac pony until the springtime."

"That was a really great move, Khaled. He left that sedan to sit all winter. Come spring, when he turned the ignition, nothing happened. He lifted the hood and learned the engine had cracked. When he discovered it would cost three hundred dollars to mend it, he asked me, 'Can you give me a push to the junkyard? I can bury the pony for fifteen dollars.'"

"And that was the last car I had until I met Mary."

"Ah, it is my turn to tell a story, for it was I, Ahmad, who phoned our Khaled to join me on a holiday in Detroit. It was 1957, and you had just received your master's degree and needed to celebrate! The Arab community was sponsoring a convention and wanted to make sure we met all the eligible Arab women who had come to America."

"Wait, my friend Ahmad. Jack does not know that when you came to America to study mechanical engineering, I was your assistant professor during your first semester at SUI. Well, for months in my class, Ahmad would just smile and nod, smile and nod. I have never known anyone who smiles more than he does! I thought he was simple, but his grades were at the top of the class. Then one day, I heard him mumbling to himself in Arabic, and I yelled, 'Why, damn you, for a month, you have shaken your head at me, but never mentioned you speak my native tongue!' It was so good to meet someone whom I could speak to with great ease and not worry about mispronouncing or using a wrong word. We became like brothers instantly. He graduated SUI and immediately obtained a job at the Westinghouse, here in Buffalo. I thank you again, Ahmad, for leading us here to Buffalo. We have enjoyed very good years here. But, back to our story:

"It was eleven years ago, on the twenty-seventh of May, when I entered into the main ballroom of the Imperial Hotel in Detroit. I remember it as if it was yesterday—the crush of Arabic-speaking young adults, laughter, and being swept up in a whirlwind of dancing to my kind of music. I felt as if I had returned home to Majd Al Krum. I found myself dancing with a short brunette whose nametag read MARY. I asked, 'Where are you from?'"

Mary piped in jubilantly. "I was born in Fort Dodge, Iowa, but my parents came from Lebanon about fifty years before."

"As I had been living in Iowa myself for almost four years, I wondered why I had not met this lovely creature before."

"Jack, I told him about a hundred times that I had a master's degree in nutrition and was working at the Mayo Clinic in Minnesota. He didn't hear a word I said, and I had to repeat myself over and over again! I thought he was deaf, but worried he was dumb. I almost gave up on him!"

"It was because I could not hear or see anything except your hypnotizing eyes, my dear Mary. It was love at first sight!"

Jack bolted up, knocked over his coffee, and called over his shoulder, "Crap, I have been sitting here all day! I should have been at practice ten minutes ago! It's been great. See you."

Art was impressed by Jack's rapid exit and remarked, "I must follow suit."

"Me, too." Ahmad stood and bowed. Khaled and Mary escorted Art back outside, and Riad serenely smiled out the garden window.

CHAPTER 2:

THE EVENING BEFORE JUNE 4, 1968

As SOON AS THE Mayflower movers had rolled out of sight, the Diab family climbed into the taxi that delivered them and their suitcases to Ahmad's A-frame, nestled in the deep woods near a trout stream. The aroma of curry greeted them long before the wiry Egyptian opened the red door. The center room was sparse but inviting. Candles were lit on every conceivable space, and in front of the glowing freestanding fireplace, a large golden velvet sofa had been placed.

At dinner, Ahmad asked Ahmeena, "Have I ever told you the story of when your dad and mom visited me on their honeymoon?"

"Many times, but tell it again."

"Ah yes, your father, while romantic, is also very frugal. During their whirlwind seven-month courtship, your mother and grandparents arranged all the wedding details, but your father was in charge of the honeymoon. He had coordinated a series of job interviews in Illinois, Indiana, Michigan, Ohio, D.C., and New York. All the companies were providing them a hotel room for two nights while in their city."

Khaled interrupted gleefully, "Yes. It was a master plan! My darling and I, alone in our new coupe--so many memories were made in that car. It was painful to consider selling her, and much better to give Jack the keys!"

"Yes, I am glad we did that small kindness, but let's not get sidetracked. You know how I love to laugh at the memory of your near arrest!"

Khaled groaned, "Ok, I will tell it. We had left our wedding guests a few hours before and were about an hour from our evening's accommodations at your aunt's South Bend home. Your mother and I were laughing and planning our lives, when a red flashing light appeared in my rearview mirror. I was shaking like a leaf as the patrolman approached and introduced himself as Officer Kasmir, then tipped his hat to both of us.

"He asked, 'Sir, do you have any idea how fast you were flying into South Bend?'

"I was so nervous, I could only stammer, 'Officer, I am sorry. We are spending the night in South Bend at my wife's sister's house. We just left a big party, and I am sorry for speeding. I won't do it again. I have no idea how fast I was going.' When he told me I was doing fifty in a thirty-five mile per hour zone, I just knew I was going to go to jail!"

"Your father exaggerates. The officer said, 'Young man, I am sorry to take you in, but you must follow me, slowly. I stress slowly. I have to take you to traffic court.' Your dad was too embarrassed to just tell the officer we were on the first night of our honeymoon, and now we were both worried we would spend our first night of marriage in traffic court!"

"Your mother held her tongue and my hand until the judge called, 'Khaled M. Diab.' I was trembling as I stood in front of him. Even before he could ask me a question, I blurted out, 'Guilty, I was speeding.' That judge commended me on my honesty, fined me one dollar for speeding, and twenty-five dollars for court costs!"

"It was hysterical. The judge smashed his gavel; your dad peeled off the bills and handed them to the judge, and we both ran out, laughing our heads off. We were back in our car, and my darling says to me, 'you see, Mary, you will never forget your wedding night, now will you?'"

Ahmad interjected, "Yes, but I want to tell Ahmeena about her mother and the mummy. You see, I had arranged the most exciting job prospect at the Westinghouse Company in Buffalo for your father. In fact, I delivered him to his interview the morning after your mother met her first mummy. I was living in a small apartment back then, and your parents and I spent the evening reminiscing. At midnight, I escorted your parents to the one and only bedroom. I intended to sleep on the couch. Around three o'clock in the morning, your mother, who had enjoyed a lot of curry the evening before, was making her way back to the kitchen for a glass of water. I heard her shriek, 'A mummy!' It was only I, Ahmad, all wrapped up in my white clothes from head to foot, for that is my custom."

"And once I knew it was you, I thought you looked just like a chrysalis in a flannel cocoon."

"Yes, and a few hours after that, I knew I would be joining the Buffalo facility. I remember your mother's face when I returned that afternoon and told her we were moving. I was to report for my position as engineer of the special projects section in ten days. We needed to locate an apartment and start packing."

"Oh Khaled, you were right, for I will never forget my honeymoon. And now, Ahmeena, we must bid these gentlemen goodnight, for tomorrow we begin a new life!" After a lot of hugging and fighting back tears, Mary led her daughter upstairs and worried over how short of breath the climb had made her.

The next morning, Ahmad drove the Diab family to the airport. On the way, Mary asked her daughter, "Have I ever told you about the time your dad first met my parents?"

"Now, Mary, that's my story; I remember it well. As you know, my dear daughter, our custom is for the prospective groom to visit the bride's family alone and ask for permission to wed. So I traveled for hours by train and taxi from Iowa City to Fort Dodge. As soon as I opened the gate of the two-story brick colonial where your grandparents have lived for sixty years and rang the bell, I knew my life would never be the same. The door swung open, and the tiniest women I had ever seen stood, waved, and chanted, 'Keffak? Ahlan Wa-sahlan. Keffak? Ahlan Wa-sahlan.' I was mystified. I am fluent in Arabic, French, and English, but never had I heard such a dialect before. Then your grandfather appeared. He stood two feet taller than your grandmother and greeted me with the typical Middle Eastern hug. Yes, that is the night I met Haddiee and Moses Habhab. He is not as tall as he was then, but remains strong and healthy. Doesn't he, Mary?"

Mary nodded and thought, My folks are still in great shape; I share their genes; I hope I have nothing to worry about. This shortness of breath is most likely anxiety over flying. How I hate flying!

"Ah well, yes, Haddiee continued to speak her own brand of English. She said, 'How are you? Please come in.' But what I heard then was Keffak? Ahlan Wa-sahlan, over and over again."

Ahmeena chirped, "Yes, Haddiee understands everything I say, but it is always a guessing game if I understand her."

"Do you know Shoo baddak tedink? Shoo baddak tedink? in Haddiee-speak?"

"Of course, it means what would you like to drink?"

"Wait," Mary said, "I wanted to tell our daughter about my father's life in America as an olive oil peddler. Moses came to America in 1905 from Lebanon. He carried fifty tins of olive oil in a burlap bag, knocked on every door he came to, and did not return home until his bag was empty. Many times, he would be gone for a week or more. Haddiee would stay home with my three brothers and two sisters, and we all were always happy and content, no matter how long he would be gone. But, when Daddy Moses appeared, the party started and went on for days!"

"What amazed me was how he became an affluent real estate broker and an active member of the Rotary. He was my inspiration to become a Rotarian myself. We had a great visit. That night, I slept in your uncle's vacated room. I dreamt I was a boy of six again in Majd Al Krum. Little Mo, your Uncle Mohammed, who now lives in Cairo, had just been born, and there was a family celebration, with hundreds in attendance. Musicians were singing familiar tunes, and then I inhaled my mother's cooking. When I opened my eyes, I was salivating. The essence was wafting in from the kitchen below. I jumped out of bed and dressed quickly. When I arrived downstairs, Haddiee was waiting. She greeted me with a smile and asked, 'Keef baddak el-eggsat?' With sudden understanding I replied, 'Oh, I like them scrambled.'"

By the time Khaled had finished his story, Ahmad had parked the car and was emptying the trunk of their bags. The three Diabs checked in and boarded the plane in relative silence. All were remembering the past. By the time their plane reached cruising altitude, Khaled's mind had taken him back to October 1948, to his ancient olive grove village of Majd Al Krum, located in Upper Galilee, just a day's walk from Nazareth. His mother, sisters, and brothers surrounded him once again at the well-worn kitchen table that had been hewn from an ancient olive tree trunk decades before. They sat in silence, waiting for the elder Mr. Diab to return from the meeting with the leaders of the community.

Khaled had just turned twenty-one and had graduated from Government Arab College in Jerusalem. He had received notice of a full scholarship and board at the university in London. He was imagining his life unfolding, when his father silently opened the front door, choking back tears.

He told his nervous family the news that shattered their happy lives. Khaled could hear as clearly now as he did then the tremor in his father's voice. "The village is surrounded by the Israeli Defense Force. Khaled, you must take your sister Khaldiyeh and leave for Lebanon tonight. I just left the village elders. We all agree that the young people who can make the journey must flee, or they might be slaughtered. Do you remember what happened on Mount Zion five months ago? On your mother's birthday, May seventeenth of this very year, two of the Christian churches and their elementary schools were shelled with mortar rounds, killing eight and wounding six scores of innocent Christian people. These Zionists do not respect innocent civilians. Until we are assured of justice and peace, you and Khaldiyeh must flee. I will remain, to keep claim to our homestead and protect the very young and very old."

Khaled's mind raced. "I have compassion for the Jewish people, but this is insanity, chasing us off our lands. I know they are acting out of a deep wound within them; the horrors of the Holocaust are unbearable to comprehend! If only the whole world had welcomed them as neighbors during the Holocaust, offering them sanctuary in their time of need, we would not be facing their weapons now!"

Mr. Diab intruded upon Khaled's contemplation with a mournful wailing, and then poured out, "These Zionists are forcing us off the land we have lived on for decades. Our family has cared for this grove for over six generations. And now the Israeli Defense Force has come to claim it as its own! We have a deed recorded in the city of Acre, just as every other landowner has! How can another claim what is legally ours? We have been caretakers of this land for generations, and a recorded deed has always been legal and binding. I cannot think of anything more unjust than to force people out of their homes and land. These trees are living, breathing beings, and their roots are entwined with our family!"

Mrs. Diab stood up, trembling, and spoke directly to Khaled. "We have always lived in peace here in Majd Al Krum. Although we have been ruled over by the Turks and the British, these Zionists are taking control without any regard for our rights! These Zionists claim to be good Jews, but they are not like our Jewish friends! No, they do not practice what our Jewish friends teach—justice, love, and common welfare! These Zionists have corrupted Judaism!"

Khaled's voice quivered. "These Zionists are secularists; they are not like our Jewish friends. But, we must get moving; I hear people gathering outside."

As the family wept, Khaled remained stoic and thought of his great-grandfather, bewailing about all the European Jews who settled in the land after the Ottoman Empire fell. "Surely, it was because he feared Western thought, not Judaism or Jewish people. We are all people of the book, and we should all honor Allah and Abraham and live in peace together. We Arabs suffer a lot as a people, because we have not accepted the good things Western thought brings, such as modern technology and medicine. There must be a balance between accepting the good and refusing what would hurt our customs and traditions. I want to help my people come into the twentieth century, but still retain our deep roots that are anchored in the God of Abraham. We cannot go backwards. We must move forward, or we will be crushed, and I pray this is not our crushing!"

When Khaled and his sister had gathered their belongings in a pillowcase, Mr. Diab spoke sternly. "Oh Khaled, how many Jewish families do we know? We know many. We have always gotten along in peace. We have gone to their weddings, and they have celebrated with us at ours. Never have we had a fight with any of our Jewish neighbors, or Christians, for that matter. We have always lived in peace and harmony in Majd Al Krum. All I want to do is care for my olive grove, as my forefathers did. The United Nations deemed Majd Al Krum Arab territory just last year, and look what is at our door! I see history repeating itself. The Jews were persecuted, and now they persecute us!"

"Look, this may be just a temporary situation. I accept charge of my sister Khaldiyeh, and will keep her safe until we may return."

"Your Uncle Mohammed and Aunt Latifah are being told the news now by your grandfather, and they will accompany you. I have a good friend in Lebanon. He owns a large olive grove, and he will help you when you arrive." Khaled watched his father write out the name of Ali Al Hussein, open the family moneybox, and hold out the entire contents with a trembling hand.

In the house next-door, Khaled's grandfather shared the same news with his second wife and their children: sixteen-year-old Latifah and fifteen-year-old Mohammed. Little Mo was barely five feet tall and loved his mother very much. Like Khaled, he had spent many months away from home in the urban center of Acre, ten miles away. Due to the rocky and wildly mountainous terrain, both boys had spent months at a time living with grandparents and missing the rest of their family. Latifah and her parents sobbed and embraced one another tightly. Little Mo had frozen in his chair, and his throat had choked up. Not until his tears had puddled upon his lap was he able to budge. Then he was glued to his mother, and all were inconsolable.

The wailing of families throughout Majd Al Krum could be heard for miles that night. Within an hour of hearing the news, the entire village lined up along the main road in town. Families hugged and stifled cries. Everyone carried pillowcases stuffed with food and a few essentials. In single file, under the cover of darkness, thousands of Palestinians set off like half of a ripped-apart chain of heartbroken people praying for wisdom and peace. The half of the chain that remained prayed for their safety. In total speechlessness, the chain of humanity set off, guided by the light of a crescent moon. Through Galilee to Lebanon, a twenty-one hour journey, over rough mountainous roads and through dark wilderness, bound the people together as only silent shared grief can.

Khaled ruminated over how the half-century-old conflict over land rights between Jews and Palestinians had become so inflamed as to force him from his family home. He remembered reading the magazines and newspapers he had pored over in the library at Jerusalem College. He visualized the pages: Balfour Declaration, November 1917. The British rulers promised a Jewish homeland in Palestine. He remembered the photo of the kings of Iraq and Syria, and Feisal Hussein executing a treaty with Jewish leader Chaim Weizman in 1919.

In 1922, Britain received a mandate from the League of Nations to create a Jewish homeland in Palestine, opening the floodgates of Jewish immigration from Europe. By the end of the decade, hundreds of Arabs and Jews had died over land rights in Palestine. In 1936, the Arabs revolted against Britain—their controllers after the fall of the Ottoman Empire and Turkish domination. Farouk became King of Egypt, and a good friend to the West. In November of 1940, Arab terrorists bombed the boat Patria, filled with Jewish immigrants at the port of Haifa. Two hundred innocent people died.

Six years later, Menachem Begin led Jewish terrorists in the destruction of the King David Hotel in Jerusalem, which was the British military and civilian headquarters. Ninety-one people died. One year later, the United Nations ordered the partition of Palestine into a Jewish state and an Arab state, with an international zone around Jerusalem. As the Jews created the state of Israel, Arab leaders condemned the United Nations' plan, and the Baath Arab Socialist party was founded in Syria. On the very day in May 1948 that Israel declared her independence, Egypt, Jordan, Syria, Lebanon, and Iraq attacked. The last newspaper Khaled read before returning home had printed the horrific news of Haganah, the underground Jewish militia's massacre of Arabs in Lydda, Ramle, and Doueimah. Khaled realized he had become a player in history and felt a deep connection to those in front and behind him. Israeli Defense Forces had surrounded his hometown, Majd El Krum, which was once a peaceful village of fruit and olive groves. A sea of people walked in single file for hours, in a dazed silence, seeking shelter and praying for peace.

Just as dawn was breaking, Little Mo whispered, "I am thirsty."

For the first time since they had started their trek eight hours prior, Khaled had enough light to actually see his family. His gut ached when he saw their cracked and swollen lips, bleeding legs scratched by thistles, and Khaldiyeh and Latifah's worn-out shoes. While Khaled and Little Mo were protected with long thick pants and closed shoes, all that the girls owned were sandals and flowing gowns. Khaled was overcome with grief and helplessness.

The tallest stranger in the queue cleared his throat and walked towards a broad-leafed carob tree a few feet away. Being a shepherd by trade, he knew the secrets of the large evergreen. At the top of the tree grew large red pods that contained sweet fruit. The broad leaves dripped with morning dew, and their edges glistened in the rising sun.

It was as if Khaled still heard the comforting voice of that shepherd saying, "Everyone, come here. Stand under this tree, and cup your hands together. Catch the dew as I shake it from the leaves. Drink the sweetest water in the land." Everyone became ecstatic as their cupped hands filled with the sweet water, and they all drank with gratitude, and then continued on their journey, with pockets stuffed with red pods, known as locust bean gum or St. John's bread. Legend has it that the locusts that the Baptist ate in the wilderness nearly two thousand years prior were from that carob plant.

Just beyond the Palestinian border, they reached the town of Bint Jubayl in Lebanon, and the line of Palestinians now broke up. The small family huddled closely and made their way through anxious crowds. Khaled remembered asking dozens of people if anyone knew Ali Al Hussein, a prosperous olive oil producer. They finally pointed towards a gathering of hundreds of people. Khaled had asked everyone who the owner of the grove was, when another traveler pointed down the grove to the water well and said, "I do not know the kind man's name, but he is at the well, welcoming us with water and bread."

The four young people waited patiently in line for their turn to receive a drink from the well. It was with great joy that they received the good news that Ali Al Hussein was the man at the well. The younger ones sat and devoured hard crusts of bread and did not pay attention to the fear in Khaled's voice as he shared their twenty-one hour journey with Ali Al Hussein. Ali fought back tears and only shrugged, handing Khaled a blanket and pointing them down the grove to the east. There, they found an unoccupied olive tree. In silence, they spread the blanket atop the dirt and roots and huddled together in the cold October night beneath the tree's broad canopy. They fell into an exhausted sleep. Khaled, Little Mo, and the young girls remained under that olive tree another night, before Khaled decided they must find shelter.

A mile from the grove, the young family found a vacant, unfinished room in an unfinished building and sat down. For two days, they moved in a cloud of unknowing and disbelief, as more refugees flooded Lebanon. Daily, Khaled ventured into the town for news, while Little Mo and the girls stayed in and held their ground.

The news was discouraging. Their meager funds were dwindling. Food was expensive and scarce. Khaled looked at his family, anticipating a life of poverty and shame. After returning home on the third day, he announced, "We must move on. I say we go to Damascus. I have my teacher's certificate with me. I will teach the children of wealthy merchants, and we will eat and sleep without fear until we can return home."

He smiled, remembering the fierce joy of Khaldiyeh and Latifah when they erupted into song and dance, and Little Mo asked, "Why not?" It was their first laugh since leaving home.

The only transportation available was a decrepit old train that had once carried livestock. Hundreds of refugees packed in like standing sardines. People relieved themselves and vomited all around the young family. After five hours, Khaled noticed the girls looked ready to pass out and announced that they must all jump off.

"I will count to twenty, and then we must all jump at the same time. Are you ready?" The girls were visibly trembling, but nodded yes. Little Mo appeared stoic, but quaked within. Khaled counted slowly as they all stood at the edge of the open car holding hands. Khaled screamed "twenty," and he, Little Mo, and Latifah jumped, but not Khaldiyeh! With astounding power Khaled ran after the train, climbed back aboard, grabbed his sister, picked her up, and jumped off once more. The siblings were scraped and bruised, but grateful to get off that wretched train. They laughed for only the second time since they had left Majd Al Krum.

The young family walked the remaining mile to Beirut, where they spent the night wide awake in a bus depot, waiting for their ride to Damascus. They were filled with idealistic, youthful hopes, until their connection arrived, carrying thousands of dazed and confused refugees.

After disembarking from the long, silent ride, Khaled led his family into a dingy gray Damascus neighborhood. He was able to afford a few nights in a sparsely furnished attic room. On the third day, he ventured alone into the center of the cradle of civilization. Around the corner from their depressing room, Khaled entered the world's most ancient shopping bazaar, sprawled along winding narrow blocks.

The Damascus streets were filled with incredible sights and smells, overwhelming Khaled's senses. His gait slowed to a shuffle as he inhaled and savored the pungent spices of meats and the sweet perfume of fresh fruits. He was amazed at the variety of the many-colored fine brocades and silks. He heard dialects and languages he had never heard before. People from the entire planet milled about, and he marveled at their varied fashions. He stopped at a booth displaying rugs and despaired at the thought of his family sleeping another night on a bare floor.

Khaled shivered once again, as he recollected the Syrian merchant with the crooked smile, who asked, "Which carpet is it that you desire?"

Khaled pointed to the thinnest scrap and asked "How much?"

The swarthy merchant replied, "Only 125 Syrian liras. It is a bargain, and it is a fine eye you have for excellent quality. I see you are a smart young man, who will not pass up my gracious offer."

Khaled was shocked into silence. The amount was five times more than he possessed. He turned to leave, as the rug merchant shouted, "How much can you spend? You cannot just walk away from me. What can you afford? You cannot treat me this way! You must answer me. How much can you spend?"

Khaled never had experienced such a verbal assault from any of the merchants in his hometown, and blurted out, "I have twenty-five Syrian liras."

The rug merchant's face clouded over with concern, and he asked, "Ah, young man, are you a refugee?"

Khaled sighed and sadly nodded.

The merchant smiled broadly as he extended his palm to receive all that Khaled had and effusively expressed, "I am so very sorry for all of you refugees. My dear boy, I will lose a lot by accepting your offer. But I feel so sorry for you. I will suffer the loss to make a poor refugee happy."

Khaled chuckled at how uplifted he had been to think he had made such a great deal. He jubilantly ran and danced his way home, proudly carrying the scrap of wool high above his head. The young family danced with joy on top of their new rug, and laughed and sang with gratitude that they would not be sleeping on a bare floor that evening. A booming knock on their door startled them into a hushed silence. Khaled opened the door and in popped their landlady.

"Just what is all the commotion about? I thought you were coming through the ceiling; you all made so much noise," she said.

Khaled proudly pointed to the rug and told of the excellent bargain he had made. The landlady stood upon the thin rug and sniffed twice. She spoke through a smirk. "Oh, I have the same rug and paid only nineteen Syrian liras for it."

Khaled remembered, I certainly learned the art of bargaining that day!

Mary glanced at her husband and knew he was back in Majd Al Krum. She closed her eyes and prayed he would not speak aloud, as she was feeling so fatigued. Khaled was oblivious to anything except his memories. He recalled the days that turned into weeks. He and Little Mo searched for work, and Khaldiyeh and Latifah spent the day locked in their room, singing sad songs and longing for home, family, and friends.

After nearly three weeks with no news, Khaled was walking through the ancient bazaar, when he recognized the hunched back of his uncle who owned the olive press in Majd Al Krum. "*Marhaba*, Uncle! Uncle Abie, *Marhaba*, it's Khaled; STOP!" he shouted, and ran towards him, with Little Mo right behind.

Uncle Abie turned and tears rolled down his weathered face. He stunned Khaled with the words spilling from between his parched lips. "Oh, Khaled, your own father waved the white flag of surrender, but there is no peace in Majd Al Krum. I was there. I am a witness to what occurred. It was awful. No, no, do not worry. Your father, mother, brothers, and sisters are all fine. After our surrender, the IDF confiscated all our weapons. Everything they demanded, we handed over."

"Then, they pointed to our neighbor Abdul, the brothers from the west grove, and Big Yassar. They lined them up in front of all our eyes and shot them in cold blood. It was so awful! The women and the children all screamed. I am ashamed to admit that I was screaming, too. I took my family away as fast as I could, and we only just arrived here yesterday."

"Abie, you break my heart and my spirit. Little Mo, go back and stay with the girls; I need to be alone and think."

Uncle Abie watched in dazed disbelief as Little Mo, with tears streaming, ran. Khaled turned onto Straight Street and began to walk to the west gate. The deep, brooding silence once again engulfed him, for it had become his dark friend.

Khaled shivered, as he was once again totally present in his past. He clearly saw his former principal from the Government Arab College in Jerusalem, Hassan Arafat, waving his arms and calling his name along the Damascus streets. "Khaled, I have been calling your name and following you for a block and a half. What is the matter with you? Why did you not hear me?"

Khaled bit his lip hard to help stifle the emotions, pouring out in a torrent then, and still close to the surface. Hassan took great pity on him, and Khaled remembered how good it had been to tell his sad tale.

Hassan spoke again. "My dear boy, Khaled, I have taken a job with the Syrian government to coordinate the influx of Palestinian refugees. Two blocks from here is the Assistant Minister of Education's office. He is in charge of all of Syrian schools and will know of any teaching jobs. Come with me now; I will introduce you and tell him you are a fine mathematics teacher."

Khaled choked back his gratitude again at the thought of such good luck. Out of such blind despair, he now saw the faint glimmer of new hope. Together, the men walked, reminiscing of old colleagues and better times. When they arrived at the large modern edifice, Khaled took a deep breath and climbed the stairs nervously. Mr. Arafat knocked on the door labeled Assistant Minister of Education.

"Come in."

Khaled felt greatly blessed. Hassan introduced him to Mr. Abdelsattar as a former student and the first in his graduating class. Mr. Abdelsattar stood and extended his hand. "Welcome. I trust my friend Mr. Arafat has brought an answer to my prayer. The school session has already started, and we need one more math teacher in the town of Hasaka."

Khaled was once again sorry he had attempted a joke by asking, "How far away from hell is it?"

Mr. Abdelsattar smiled weakly and replied, "About 160 kilometers away in northeast Syria. Tomorrow morning, catch the morning train at seven o'clock to Aleppo for a twelve-hour ride. There are usually enough chairs in the

Aleppo depot for all to sleep in until the next morning, when the buses arrive. Make sure you ask for the direct bus to Hasaka, and you will arrive there in two days' time."

"Two days on a bus? What does it do, transport livestock to and from the market?" Khaled had thought he had made another joke.

Mr. Abdelsattar seriously replied, "Yes, my boy, it does. It makes frequent stops, but it will be an adventure; look on the bright side."

Khaled took the advice and ran home to tell the others that they were moving on. At dawn the next day, carrying everything they owned tied up in sheets, the young family walked in the frigid cold to the train depot a mile away. The train was unheated, and the four huddled closely and imagined out loud what the future would offer them. When they arrived at the depot, they were grateful to find four chairs together and slept until dawn.

They rose to the aroma of strong coffee, which a peddler was offering at an exorbitant price. When their bus arrived, Khaled realized Mr. Abdelsattar had not exaggerated. People, goats, sheep, and chickens were spilling out from all sides. They traveled on rocky dirt roads and saw only homes made of mud. By evening, they were the only ones left on the bus, and Khaladiyeh remarked to her brother, "If your city is made up of mud homes, I am not getting off this bus."

It was one month since they had left their comfortable home in Majd Al Krum. Khaled's thoughts frequently alternated between suicide and homicide. He feared the young girls would be forced into prostitution if the teaching job did not materialize. He could not bear the thought. Hope fought with despair with every turn of the wheels on the over-packed bus.

By midnight, they arrived at the town of Hasaka and checked into the nearest hotel. Khaled was aghast when he opened his thin wallet and handed over the first night's rent. They were now out of money, and Khaled was to report to the school within a few hours. They trudged down the dark hallway and heard every sound that emanated from every room. Their senses were assaulted by a damp, musky smell that permeated the tattered building.

Khaled opened the door to their room and gasped. In the center, four thin mattresses lay on a wooden floor. A chipped table, a cracked water pitcher, and a naked light bulb set in an old wine bottle were the only furnishings. The girls immediately fell asleep on their mats, while Little Mo sat leaning against the grimy gray wall and fell asleep a moment later. Khaled sat opposite him, wide awake with his dark, tormenting thoughts.

At three o'clock in the morning, the door shot open, and in charged two Syrian policemen. The girls screamed. Khaled ran to protect them from the terror of the intrusion. The police accused them of prostitution, and Khaled's worst nightmare seemed to be happening. Haltingly, in fear and trembling, Khaled recounted the events of the past month as the police examined their papers. It was nearly dawn before the police were satisfied, and let them be.

Khaled's dark mood turned bitter. He had not slept in two days. He sternly cautioned Little Mo to bolt the room and keep the girls quiet until he returned from his day at State High School. He walked the mile in darkness to the new large edifice in the best part of town. Khaled's mood soured the longer he stood in front of the locked school building on that cold, damp morning.

When the regal Kurdish principal, Mr. Hamza, arrived, he greeted Khaled warmly saying, "My dear friend, Mr. Abdelsattar has sent me word you will make an excellent teacher. Come with me, I will give you a tour of our school before your students arrive."

In a daze, Khaled followed Mr. Hamza, unable to focus on anything other than the anguish and exhaustion he felt. When they reached Khaled's classroom, he barely heard Mr. Hamza introduce him to the students excitedly. "My children, the minister of education has sent to us your new mathematics teacher, Mr. Khaled. He will be the best teacher you have ever had. I am sure you will all have a good and productive day."

Mr. Hamza waved goodbye and left Khaled looking at the faces of thirty adolescent boys. Khaled picked up the math book and demanded to know just what they did and did not know. The bravest boy in the class blurted out indignantly, "What is your problem? We just want to learn, not fight with you."

He thought, I have had many a dark mood, and I have burst into verbal tirades. But that day it really was all directed at the events of the past four weeks, not toward a poor, unsuspecting class. I am still sorry and embarrassed that I replied, "You all may be too stupid to learn anything, but I will try."

The boys kept their eyes averted and never spoke another word in that classroom that day. At the end of the school day, the students filed into Mr. Hamza's office demanding he fire Khaled. Mr. Hamza found a trembling Khaled sitting in the darkened classroom. He quietly approached and softly asked, "What happened in here?"

Khaled remembered acutely how suicidal he was at that low point. But then, Mr. Hamza had spoken so gently, "Is it money? Do you need money?" Then he opened his wallet, took out a month's worth of wages, and handed it to Khaled. "Now Khaled, go home, feed your family, and get some sleep. Report back to work tomorrow morning."

He gratefully whispered, "Thanks." And the burden of the past month immediately lifted and, for the first time since he had left Majd Al Krum, Khaled believed he had a future with hope.

Mr. Hamza firmly stated, "Do not thank me, but help another whenever you can."

On the airplane, Ahmeena had grown tired of her book, turned to her father, and demanded, "Why haven't you told your story of coming to America for the first time? You always tell me that one whenever we fly anywhere!"

Khaled remained silent, for he was now absorbed in remembering December of 1948, when the UN General Assembly passed Resolution 194, affirming the rights of Palestinians to either return home or be compensated for their property. By January of 1949, seven hundred thousand Muslims and fifty thousand Christians had become refugees. In May, Israel was admitted to the United Nations.

In September of 1949, he received orders from the minister of education to transfer to Dayr az Zawr, a metropolitan town sixty miles away. When he arrived home that night, he announced to his family, "I am being transferred to Dayr az Zawr, and the time has come for us to part. Israel is offering a short-term concession to those younger than eighteen years of age to return home. As long as the parents remained on the land, their children may come home to them. Little Mo is eligible to return, too, but I am twenty-two and will not be allowed to go back.

Khaled continued, "When Resolution 194 is enforced, I will be able to travel freely, but until then, I am an alien here in Syria. I have become an exile from my own beloved country, Palestine! My God! I am labeled a Palestinian refugee, but I am one Palestinian who refuses to be a refugee!"

He was crestfallen when the girls erupted in ecstatic jumping, dancing, singing, and laughing, but understood they had missed their parents a lot. Little Mo glowed. "I will be so happy to see mother again, but I will return to you and finish my education as planned! I don't want to be like a refugee either. I want a future with hope!"

As soon as the authorities verified the Diab parents wanted their children home, the trio set off in high spirits, and Khaled traveled lightly. When Little Mo returned three weeks later, Khaled had moved into a small apartment consisting of two rooms and a bath. For the first time since he had left Majd Al Krum, he enjoyed indoor plumbing. He hired an old, deeply wrinkled woman named Oum Faheem to clean and cook. It soon became apparent Oum Faheem boiled the taste out of everything, but Khaled did not have the heart to fire her. He worked long hours at both the all-girls and all-boys schools. After a tasteless dinner, he tutored Little Mo and the neighborhood children.

One day Little Mo wandered home from the all-boys school down a new alley. It was the dumping site for the textile factory, and he stumbled upon exquisite scraps of damask and velvet. He ran home and told Khaled. They had the makings of furniture. The two young men attached the multi hued fragments in a patchwork, stuffed thick cotton underneath, and then attached it to planks of wood.

"Now that we have a sofa, let's have a party!" Little Mo exclaimed, and Khaled happily agreed. That Friday night, the teachers from each school arrived. He cooked shish kebobs, and they all laughed with abandonment and great camaraderie. He had met Suad in the all-girls school's teachers' lounge during his first day on the job. Suad taught languages and history, and shopped in French boutiques. Her hair was blonde and her eyes were deep green. She mesmerized him. There were many more Friday-night gatherings at the home of Little Mo and Khaled, and Suad looked forward to every one.

After two years of teaching in Dayr az Zawr, Khaled knocked on the door of the principal's office. Mrs. Dahham called out, "Come in," and he entered the office.

"Excuse me, do you have a moment? Thank you. You see, Suad and I have confessed our love for one another. I am hoping you will be my mediator with her parents. I want to ask her to marry me, and we believe they will approve."

"I will gladly represent you to Suad's father," stated the tall Kurdish woman, who wore English clothes. That very day, she set up a meeting for the following evening. The entire clan filled the house, and Suad was radiant with the expectation of marriage.

After quietly listening to Mrs. Dahham and Suad's parents speak glowingly of the union, a brother-in-law blurted out, "If you do not have Suad marry my cousin, I will divorce your daughter. If you allow Suad to marry a refugee, I will leave this family!" The family meeting dissolved into tears and anger, and Mrs. Dahham was grateful for Khaled's absence.

Mrs. Dahham waited in Khaled's classroom the next morning. As soon as he entered, she gave him a hug and spoke gently. "Khaled, Suad's brother-in-law is a very successful doctor. He insists that Suad must marry his cousin, or he will divorce Suad's sister. Suad is in love with you. But her parents are unable to give her their blessing, and she is unable to defy them."

Rage erupted within Khaled, a rage that had been brewing since he had left Majd Al Krum three years prior. "To hell with your Syrian wedding customs--I am going to America!"

Ahmeena was growing impatient and loudly roused her father back to the present. "Daddy, come on, what are you thinking about? I want to hear about your first trip to America!"

"Ok, I was just remembering what led up to that life-altering decision. After suffering a broken heart, I realized that the time had come to move on. So I sent out twenty-one applications to American universities. Within a few months, eighteen acceptance letters and scholarship offers filled my kitchen table. I borrowed the US map from the geography department and spread it out upon the table. Little Mo stuck straight pins into the states where I had been accepted. After twenty-one pins poked out from around the United States, Little Mo announced, 'OK, now Khaled, I think Washington State is too close to Canada. It will be too cold,' and he pulled that pin back out.

"'Now, Khaled, Georgetown sounds too expensive. Forget it,' and Mo pulled that pin too. Little Mo had finally reduced the number of pins down to one, the State University of Iowa! We both agreed that because it was in the center of the country, the middle would be just right! Besides, they offered me a full tuition scholarship in engineering, and a fifty percent reduction on room and board.

"The only problem was that the American Embassy required at least one thousand dollars to bring into America with me. I had only saved two hundred dollars. Mrs. Dahhman took pity on me and wrote out a check, but I had to return it to her after showing the men at the embassy. I did not mention I was not going to cash it. I just presented it to them and allowed them to form their own conclusion. Many friends told me I was crazy to go to America with only two hundred dollars. They all received the same reply: there are two hundred million Americans making a living over there, and if I cannot do the same, it will be totally my fault.

"So on a cold morning in 1953, I bid goodbye to Little Mo, who had now grown a few more inches and was attending Damascus University. I can still smell that Turkish ship I boarded in Beirut, going to Naples. They offered steerage to students at a 40 percent discount, and I met an exotic Egyptian coed who spoke in Arabic, saying, 'Where are you going, my happy friend?'"

"I boldly replied, 'to America; why don't you come with me?' My dear, we flirted for hours as we crossed the Mediterranean Sea towards Naples, where I would board my first plane to America. We laughed and joked for so long; we both had become giddy. By the time I told her how I learned to speak English, she had become dizzy from the rolling current. I remained blissfully unaware that a storm was moving in.

"I told her about the summer before I entered the fourth grade, when a family friend told me that English is Arabic backwards. All summer, I practiced saying everything backwards. So, instead of saying 'my name is Khaled Diab,' I would say '*baid Delahk si eman ym*.' I was fluent in this English, and everyone I would speak to would look at me in astonishment! Surely I was speaking such good English; it was above their heads! I spoke my English so well, they could not understand a word I said! Then, in the seventh grade, when we studied Shakespeare, I was 'theeing' and 'thouing' everyone everywhere!"

Ahmeena joyfully erupted. "This is the best part!"

"Oh, you like the fact that this striking beauty had become so nauseated she vomited upon my new shoes on a very windy day!"

"Well, I like it better that you then hurled onto her new shoes!"

"How about that story of my first friend after I disembarked? I can still see that dirty--well, ah, friendly Italian in a blue pea coat and green woolen hat saying, 'Ah, my friend, are you new in town?'

"Since I had just gotten off the boat, I answered him truthfully. 'Yes, I just got off that boat and must get to the Rome airport by tomorrow morning. At noon I fly to America!' That interested Italian suggested we both take in the town, and I was just dumbfounded! Why, I was only off the boat for five minutes, and I had already made a friend! We walked down the street until we reached the doorway of the town's largest hotel, and I said I would like to check in and freshen up, for I smelled like puke.

"At that moment, the door attendant appeared and scowled at the man in the blue coat with the green hat, and started to swear. 'Get out of here, you filthy thief, or I'll call the cops on you!'

"With that, he turned and ran, and I sank to the ground. The doorman sniffed, and then spoke. 'You need a bath, my friend. That nasty man is the biggest thief in town, and he would have rolled you over in an instant and stolen everything you had.'

"I checked into a room and did not venture out until dawn the next day, to catch the first bus to Rome. After arriving at the airport terminal, I was awed by the mass of humanity and invigorated by their energy. The terminal attendants were efficient, yet brusque. After nearly two days and many plane changes, I flew to America on a cold November night. As the plane circled the airport above New York City, I was mesmerized by the lights of the cars that snaked below. After disembarking, I found my way through the main hall and boarded a bus labeled Holiday Inn.

"After I checked in to my room, I spent the remainder of the night wide awake and anxious to board the train that would take me to Iowa City. I arrived at the railroad station with plenty of time to explore before my train departed, and I wandered about, astonished at all I heard and saw. These Americans are amazing, so busy, and always rushing about. They must all have very urgent business, I thought, as I was jostled aside by the crush of rush hour.

"A vendor shouted, 'Hot dogs, fresh hot dogs,' and oh, how my eyes widened in disbelief. I cannot to this day believe that these Americans, who are so rich, eat dogs!"

Ahmmena quipped, "So, what did you think, that they shot them in the street? Did you think that they grew them on farms?"

"I have never found out. But I do remember the eleven-hour train ride to Iowa City and the views of huge modern metropolises, vintage rural towns, dairy farms, cornfields, and open green countryside. It was just before nine on a blustery night, when my train pulled into the station, and the conductor's voice boomed, 'Iowa City.'

"There I was, in short sleeves and thin pants, but I was so excited. I was the first to disembark, and immediately started shivering. It must have been 20 degrees that night! I anxiously scanned the crowd, hoping the foreign student advisor would be there to greet me. And there he was, the ruddy and robust Jim Miller, who stood by the main exit and held up a sign that read, 'State University of Iowa for Khaled M. Diab.'

"I waved triumphantly to him, and boomed as I approached, 'I am Khaled!'

"Jim looked perplexed and asked, 'What's the deal, man? Where's your coat? It's below freezing outside. Let's get your bags.'

"I hated to tell him that I did not own a coat, only a few more changes of clothes, and I was carrying everything in my bag. He shook his head and said, 'Here, take my coat, I am too hot, anyway, with this sweater on underneath.' I gratefully followed Jim to the car, and piled in for the drive to the university. Then I was introduced to my roommate, a strong former farm boy with large, rough hands.

"He smiled and shook my hand so hard I felt it in my toes! 'Hi, I am Jim Taylor.'

"I asked, 'Is everyone in America named Jim?'

"Jim Miller responded, 'No, and tomorrow we will be taking you to meet Mr. J.C. Penney and get you some appropriate clothes for the cold Iowa winter.' Early that next morning, Jim Taylor escorted me to the university cafeteria, where I ate my first bowl of corn flakes. Jim introduced me to every student who passed, and everyone sat and spoke awhile. It was hours before we drove to the mall and entered JC Penney. I was rendered speechless in the huge parking lot, and enraptured by the immaculate merchandise and sales people, who did not bargain and happily gave away change. I chose an overcoat with a fur collar, then nearly choked when I was reminded that my funds had dwindled to less than one hundred dollars.

"When we returned to the car, I told Jim Miller, 'I have a slight problem. In order to get to America, a friend gave me a one-thousand-dollar check to assure the American Embassy I could support myself. I had to return the check without cashing it, and have only a few weeks worth of money with me. I need a job, or I will be sent back to Syria.'

"Jim took pity on me, and I am forever grateful. He said, 'Listen, if we tell the university you lied to get in, they will send you packing. If we tell the immigration office the truth, they will deport you. I will tell them both you lost your money and need a job.'

"By the next week, I was dressed in a white cotton apron and introduced to the university's kitchen. Another young man named Jim demonstrated to me how to wash the dishes. Steaming hot water clouded the air over the never-ending stream of plates and utensils that kept arriving on carts. I was instructed to scrape the dried food off under boiling water, and then place the plates and utensils onto a conveyor belt. I dissolved into a hysterical tirade, triggered by the culture shock. In my homeland, only women or slaves wash dishes, and I blurted out to dishwashing Jim, 'I was a respected teacher in Syria; now I am a slave!'

"I continued in Arabic, cursing, swearing, and beating my chest, while dishwasher Jim grinned broadly and said, 'You're nuts. You're not a slave and neither am I. I am attending the university to become a doctor. Settle down, do your job, and when we get our break, I'll introduce you to my friends. There's always a great crowd out there eating together, and you will see this is just a job. Someone has to do it. Mostly, though, it's a great time to use your imagination and imagine you are somewhere else.'

"I thought, Hmmm, I am glad to hear you have friends. They must be nice people; they eat with slaves. And yes, I can imagine being somewhere else, and wish I was! Jim shrugged, shook his head, and returned to scraping dried food. He was oblivious to my dark mood. I repeatedly sighed deeply, and disdainfully plunged into the task I found demeaning and emasculating.

"After four hours of silently fuming, I heard dishwasher Jim announce, 'Come on Khaled. Let's take a break.'

"Gladly, I removed my apron and entered the bustling cafeteria. We loaded up a tray with food, and Jim escorted me to a table packed with faculty and students. When Jim told the tale of my hysterics, everyone laughed, while I fumed. My soon-to-be mentor, Professor Harding, had been observing. When he stood to leave, he said, 'Khaled, in America all work is respected, and all work is necessary for us to live.'

"Those inquisitive students began softening my heart with their questions and rapt attention when I spoke of my homeland. I returned to the kitchen that day with a new attitude, and began calling dishwasher Jim 'Doctor Jim'!"

"Now, tell me about how you got your job with Professor Harding."

"Well, the next six weeks were a blur of studying to catch up. I arrived after the term had begun, and was experiencing great difficulty in Professor Harding's manufacturing process course. The new language about lathes and rivets mystified me, and I feared I would not master it. While the other students went home for the Christmas break, I spent from dawn until dusk in the lab. At the end of the semester, Professor Harding announced to the accelerated manufacturing process class, 'Young people, you all are doing excellent work. However, one of you has excelled beyond the class average of 92 percent. Khaled Diab's hard work has placed him at the top of the class, with a consistent 100 percent on every test and every paper.'"

"I flushed with pride and then blurted out, 'Ok, so if I am so great, why don't you give me a job as your assistant, and then I can quit washing dishes?' And on that day, I became an assistant professor of manufacturing processes. My life changed again."

The stewardess appeared with beverages and snacks as the pilot announced they would be landing in Orlando in less than ninety minutes. Mary had fallen asleep, and Khaled winked at Ahmeena. She knew he wanted to be quiet, too. She reopened her book and became lost in the pages, as Khaled remembered himself with Professor Harding, crunching multicolored leaves beneath their feet that bracing autumn day. It was as if Professor Harding once again stood next to him and announced, "Khaled, last Christmas you locked yourself up in the lab, and a month later, became an assistant professor. What surprise do you have for me in the coming new year?"

Khaled chuckled. "I know you have been asking me to meet some friends of yours. I may be ready to comply."

Professor Harding smirked. "Don't worry. We won't try to convert you, at least not at our first meeting! Seriously, I have been sharing your exodus story from Palestine with my Bible history class. They are fascinated with the land where Jesus walked. I know your faith is deeply personal, and you do not like to debate. I have explained to them that you would only come to share your experiences of growing up in the land we call holy."

Khaled nodded, "Exactly."

"Okay, Khaled, how about attending our next meeting on this coming Wednesday? Everyone brings a dish, and we eat, relax, and laugh out loud. After the fellowship, we will give you the floor, and you will teach us about the land we call holy."

"Then that's settled. I will meet you in the lab Wednesday. Now let us get back to tomorrow's lesson. Here is my plan."

Khaled and Professor Harding continued their walk through the campus, oblivious to anything except their discussion of manufacturing processes. On Wednesday, an hour after dusk, Khaled and Professor Harding entered the social hall of Trinity Church, built in 1803. They descended into the basement of the red brick sanctuary and were greeted by gales of laughter.

A hush fell over the crowd when Gloria shouted out, "Hi, Professor Harding. Is that Mr. Khaled?"

"Yes, this is Khaled. His proper name is Mr. Diab."

"Well, pardon me, Mr. Diab," she said, and she held out her hand and dazzled him with a brilliant smile and her auburn hair.

Khaled blushed and gently shook her hand. He gazed in wonderment at all the smiling Christians who had encircled him. He had never seen so much big hair and so many white teeth. Khaled shook hands and nodded to everyone, and then he was led to the buffet table. His eyes widened at the strange spread. "This green wiggling matter with small white puffs--what is this called?"

"Ambrosia," Gloria told him, as she placed a blob on his plate and continued, "I'll walk you through." She scooped a sampling of each onto a plate. "This is chicken salad, potato salad, macaroni salad, tuna salad, and corn bread."

"But everything is white! How can you tell it apart?" Khaled exclaimed.

Gloria laughed. "I know what you mean. It is pretty bland, with all of that mayonnaise and all. By the way, I just graduated from NYU, and am home, regrouping. In January, I begin teaching history at a high school in Manhattan."

Jimbo McCracken chirped in, "Yeah, Gloria is our black sheep. She went away to the big city for four years, and now she's all that and more. We just aren't in her league anymore; my heart's breaking."

Everyone within hearing stifled a laugh, and then began eating. Jimbo never took his big blue eyes off Khaled the entire evening. Khaled was mesmerized by all the white food, and reluctantly took a bite. A shiver ran through him as he thought, "I must bring some *zatar* next time."

When all the food had been devoured, Professor Harding announced, "My friends, I have been looking forward to this day. My life has become much richer because of my friendship with this man, Khaled Diab. He is a man who exemplifies what perseverance will reap. He has a forgiving spirit, although he has suffered a lot. His good humor never fails, and his expertise as a professor has been a great benefit to me and all our SUI students. Well, I could go on and on, but he has come here tonight to share about the land we all call holy."

The group applauded as the Professor sat down and motioned for Khaled to rise. "Thank you for your hospitality. Hospitality is very important in my culture. We always say to our guests, 'Eat as much as you love me.' I have eaten a lot tonight; I hope it was all kosher." Gloria guffawed, but everyone else shared a quizzical glance.

Khaled sighed. "Well, let me tell you of my village Majd Al Krum. It is a village with roots that go back through many centuries. Five generations of my family have lived in the same home and have worked in the same olive grove. We supported ourselves by harvesting the olives, and my uncle would press them into oil. We bartered for goods with our oil, and we lived in peace and very pleasantly until--" Khaled's eyes misted over, and it was a long moment before he continued. "Ah well, yes, some of the trees in our grove go back to Roman times."

"You mean, when Jesus was walking around?" Jimbo McCracken demanded.

"Yes, it's possible that Jesus may have taught under a Majd Al Krum olive tree. Nazareth is just a day's walk away, and five days' journey from Bethlehem."

"So, do you believe in Jesus?" Jimbo sputtered.

Khaled inhaled and spoke gently. "I believe he taught the Golden Rule. I believe that rule says we are to treat others as we would wish to be treated."

"Yeah, but how about--"

Jimbo was cut off in mid-thought as Professor Harding took command. "My friends, Khaled has graciously joined us to share about the Holy Land. I assured him we would not question him on matters of religion at this time. If he ever decides to join us again, that will be the time."

A collective wave of relief passed through the group, and Khaled began to regale them with stories about weeklong wedding feasts, holiday celebrations, and colorful cousins. By ten o'clock, Khaled had talked himself dry and announced, "Thank you for your kind attention. It was good to talk about my homeland and family again."

Everyone pleaded with him to return. He agreed to return the following week. As they left the building, Jimbo McCracken wrapped his arm around Khaled's shoulder and whispered, "My brother told me that Muslims have tails. What happened to yours?"

A rage swept through Khaled, and he sighed deeply three times before he turned and looked deep into the arrestingly big blue eyes of Jimbo to reply, "Oh, I lost it on the boat coming over, but that's another story."

"You're ok, Khaled. I was leery about meeting a Muslim; I thought you'd be different, somehow. You're alright, though, Mr. D." Jimbo was struggling in his first semester of community college, and found Khaled to be very exotic.

After a few weeks, Khaled found he was looking forward to the Trinity Church meetings more and more, for a friendship with Gloria had developed. Three months of Wednesday meetings led to their spending every Saturday together. They always picnicked in the park and spoke from their deepest hearts. Gloria declined the New York job. She still lived in her parents' home and began substitute teaching.

By June of that year, she signed a contract to teach full-time at the local community college, starting in the fall. Khaled enjoyed her quick wit and watching her athletic frame and flying hands, which helped her express her thoughts. By July, the two were seriously considering marriage. By August, they were arguing more often than agreeing. Gloria paced around their favorite tree, exclaiming, "Are you telling me you do believe in the virgin birth? I have a really hard time with that one! That amazes me--Muslims believe it!"

"Yes, Muslims understand Jesus was born of the Virgin Mary, by the command of God, through the Spirit of God."

"Then why don't you believe Jesus is God?"

"It is not what I was taught from my elders. I was taught Jesus was a great prophet, who spoke the truth and preached the true gospel: the good news that God loves all creation and will judge us all according to our hearts and our good deeds. This I believe, and this is the good news, isn't it?"

"Ok, good, we agree! Why can't you just believe one more thing, like me?" Gloria pleaded.

"Gloria, I am a product of my culture. My tradition and my family are what make me who I am. We believe everyone is a child of God, and the Ten Commandments should guide us all. The commandments teach us to honor our parents. I honor my parents, my family, and my culture by practicing my religion as I have been taught. You are not respecting my culture, my tradition, or my family when you insist I must believe just as you do. Besides, I am a scientist. I need more facts."

"But Khaled, what about hell? Aren't you afraid of going to hell?"

"Oh, Gloria, I do not live according to fear. I love God and worship him, not out of fear, but out of love. He is the Creator of the universe, and of every living thing that ever has or will be. I believe God wants us to get along, not fight, and not debate improvable ideas. Both of our religions teach us so many of the same things. Why can't you focus on where we agree, and leave the rest up to God?"

Gloria broke down and cried, "I can see it your way, but my parents will never give their blessing unless you convert!"

"Now do you understand what you are asking me to do? You cannot hurt your parents by marrying without their blessing, and I cannot marry someone who insists I hurt mine."

The young couple stood staring at each other for some time before Khaled said, "I decided to come to America after not being accepted by the family of the woman I loved. She loved me. But, her parents were dissuaded from giving us their blessing. She would not hurt her parents by marrying without their blessing. She chose to honor her family and sacrificed me. You cannot hurt your family by marrying without their blessing, and I cannot hurt mine by converting to another religion, when I am well guided by the one they taught me."

On that day in July, Khaled quit going to Trinity Church and never again saw Gloria.

By the time the plane circled high above Orlando's modest McCoy Airport, Mary had awakened and exclaimed, "How beautiful and green and open this countryside is. Oh, Khaled, I am so excited! I am also doubly glad you were able to find a home for us without me. That last episode I suffered a few days after Martin Luther King's death was another 'left to the liver,' as Art would say."

Khaled whispered, in the hope that Ahmeena was not paying any attention, "Mary, how are you feeling now? I think we should have postponed this move. That last attack of yours shook me up."

Ahmeena shook her head and exclaimed, "I was hysterical, too! You turned blue and couldn't speak. That was too scary, Mom."

Mary enfolded her daughter in a hug and cast a scowl at Khaled. "Look, I am fine. We have a referral from Dr. Stollerman, an appointment next week with his prized chief resident, who now lives in Orlando, and my records are packed in my suitcase. Relax. I feel fine. I want to look outside, too--oh, how incredible this view is!"

Khaled thought of the night she told him and still felt bad about his gruff reaction: "What do you mean? You have been short of breath and have an abnormal chest x-ray? What do you mean, you have sarcoid plaques? Those little patches on your face and throat--is that what you mean? Why didn't you tell me you were not feeling well? Every night, I come home, and you say everything is fine! You make me crazy; if things are not fine, I deserve to know!"

He took no comfort in Mary's understanding reassurances of how busy he was, and her gratitude over what a great provider he was. He felt like a fraud. He was terrified of the thought of losing Mary and had lashed out before he even realized what he was saying. He had been working many extra hours on his latest top-secret defense mission, and could not share much with her. He remembered taking the day off from work to be with her for the initial biopsy that confirmed the diagnosis. She had begun the treatment of massive doses of Prednisone just the year before.

"Hmmm," he murmured aloud.

Mary turned to him. "What did you say?"

"Oh Mary, I was just thinking of how much I love you."

CHAPTER 3:

A Celt, an Arab, and a Roman

BELOW THE DRONE OF the engines, Dr. Jake Hunter cursed as he fly-cast his bass popper into the tannic, tinted waters of Buck Lake. "Damn, that's the fourth plane to land today. Now with Disney being built in our backyard, it will soon be forty, then four hundred, then four thousand, no doubt. Here I am, surrounded by lily pads and cypress trees, being observed by deer and cougar, and people are going to start pouring in here. All this talk of Orlando becoming a resort destination--man, this pisses me off; why can't people leave things as God made them, open and green? Places to be quiet, places of silence, places to just be--God have mercy on us, if what I feel in my bones is happening here in citrus land and cattle country; everyone's selling out! Damn, financial greed will be the destruction of nature and a most unholy thing. Please, God, don't let the Mormons sell out; these thousands of acres of virgin land need to be protected. This is home for your trusting creatures, and where I run to every chance I get, away from all the demands and pressures of being a thirty-year-old internist in Winter Park! God, you know I don't mean to whine; I am very grateful for my life, my work, and my family. Thank you, but if I can't get totally away and alone from it all, I'd go berserk! This is church for me; here in the silence of nature, I hear you most clearly. Hmm, it makes me wonder about my Celtic roots. God, I think those old Druid dudes were onto something. They lived and breathed your presence in nature, in shady places by water--thin places where the veil between the visible world and invisible is thin, indeed. As the great Celtic teachers taught, the grand volume of God's utterance is the word of God in creation. Creation is to be preserved, enjoyed, and tended. All ground is holy, and this is church for me--except when those damn planes buzz over."

A mile away, the real estate agent who would drive them to their new home was greeting the Diab family. The walk-through was scheduled for that very evening, and the closing was scheduled for the following day.

"Hello, Dr. Diab, how was your flight?" The sandy haired James O'Hara fingered the brim of his straw hat and nodded his head towards Mrs. Diab.

"Just fine, James. This is the family I told you so much about." Khaled shook the young man's hand, and introductions were shared and suitcases retrieved from the lone baggage carousel that was at the end of the long, low terminal.

Outside, the steam from the cement wafted around them, as they walked towards the realtor's late-model Ford. "You just missed a typical summer afternoon's thunderstorm. They can be fierce, but they don't last too long." The entourage enjoyed the air-conditioning blowing against their sweaty faces once the car began to move. James maintained a running commentary about schools and restaurants, as the Diabs gazed at the endless orange groves that lined the highway.

"It's great that your furniture isn't arriving for two more days. You will be residing at the Langford Hotel, and will have time to explore the many fine shops that line Park Avenue and lead to the Tiffany Art Museum. Just next door to your hotel is the Winter Park library. Ahmeena, do you like to read?"

After Ahmeena rattled off a dozen titles of the books she had read in the last few weeks, Mary inquired, "Mr. O' Hara, why do we keep turning through these citrus trees at such sharp right angles? Why doesn't the road go straight through the groves?"

"Mrs. Diab, it is because hidden within these orange groves are treasures to be protected: hundreds of lakes and wetlands, which are home to deer, panthers, gators, turtles, and more birds than you can imagine. Every chance I get, I spend out on the lake, just enjoying the scenery. The real beauty of Florida is clearly visible when you are in the water. I suppose the Garden of Eden was something similar: lots of clear, healthy water."

Khaled shook his head. "Yes, I know exactly what you mean. And did you know the Garden of Eden is thought to have been in Iraq?"

"Never heard that," Mr. O' Hara offered tentatively, while the car turned onto an oak-lined street filled with an eclectic assortment of houses.

Mary gasped, "Oh, tell me this is our street. I can see a lake! Khaled, is that Lake Conway?"

"Yes, Mary, this is our lake, and our house is right there." Khaled pointed, as James turned up the drive of a rambling brick ranch home with an enormous oak tree in the front yard. Mr. O'Hara unlocked the front door and revealed the white tile and marble that filled the threshold. Mary immediately imagined her kitchen table placed before the French doors looking out at the miles of clear blue water, the curved expanse of St. Augustine grass, and the neat rows of citrus and papaya trees.

"Oh, it is beautiful; I can barely take it all in." Mary spoke to Khaled and took his hand as Ahmeena darted down the hallway, exploring.

An hour and a half later, they were back in the car, just as the sun was setting. As Mr. O'Hara started to drive, a banged-up blue Suburban with a diesel engine and a johnboat strapped on top lumbered by, and a handsome man with piercing blue eyes and a baseball cap nodded in their direction. Mr. O'Hara waved and explained, "That's the doctor who lives on the cul-de-sac at the end of your road. He built that two-story brick Tudor on three lots a few years ago, and has a household full of kids, probably one about Ahmeena's age. If you need a good doctor, you can't do better than Jake Hunter. He has an office on West Park Avenue, just up the road from the Langford Hotel. Yeah, the Langford is the place to stay when in Orlando. The hotel's restaurant is open late, and on weekends, there is always live entertainment. I already verified your reservations before I picked you up at the airport. That's great that Martin Marietta is picking up your tab and all your moving expenses. You must be a pretty important man, Dr. Diab."

"What is important to me is that my family is secure and happy."

Mary whispered, "Khaled, I believe that is the doctor I have an appointment with next week. Isn't that serendipity?"

Khaled nodded and felt at peace. After Ahmeena had been tucked in for the night, Khaled announced, "Mary, I feel like a scotch. Do you mind if I go down to the bar and get one?"

"Certainly, dear, you go. But I am ready for a shower and bed. Khaled, don't be long, dear," she cautioned.

Khaled entered the smoky, cavern-like bar, and quickly sat at the counter. A dark-eyed, raven-haired man with a large hooked nose and deeply tanned skin approached and asked, "What will it be, my friend? What can I mix you?"

"Just a scotch, house brand. Tell me, what is your name, barkeep?"

"Jim."

"Jim? I have met thousands of Jims and Jameses with every nickname imaginable. But, I have never met a Jim who looked like you."

Jim laughed and said in Arabic, "My real name is Mohammed. But I wasn't making very good tips until I became Jim. I was fortunate enough to have a sponsor to get me out of the Shaltilla refugee camp. I am currently attending Rollins College on scholarship. I work every night at this bar, and all day I apply myself to the study of law."

Khaled was astounded. "I, too, spent time in Shatilla. I have sponsored four young men from there myself, and they have all graduated college with honors, and have excellent jobs and happy families."

The men swapped stories of Shatilla, and Khaled felt incredibly connected to his roots when Jim mentioned his best friend Hassan, who happened to be the third man Khaled had sponsored. Finally Khaled said, "Enough old memories. I just flew in from Buffalo a few hours ago, and haven't seen a newspaper or heard the news all day. What's new in the outside world today?"

"Well, I am not up-to-speed either, but I will turn on the TV. It's time now for the eleven o'clock newscast."

As soon as the TV that hung from the ceiling came on, Khaled became nauseated. A video clip of Robert Kennedy lying on a floor, bleeding, as his wife knelt at his side, kept replaying, as the reporter spoke. "A lone gunman, named Sirhan Sirhan, has been apprehended at the scene here in the Ambassador Hotel. Robert Kennedy had just delivered a rousing speech and was leaving through the rear exit when the lone gunman, Sirhan Sirhan, shot him. Now, we wait in anxious anticipation, as to the fate of the Democratic candidate for president. No word yet on his condition, but as you can see clearly by the tape, the senator has suffered a severe injury. Let us hope and pray it is not fatal."

Khaled was aghast. "A beautiful day has turned into darkness. Please turn it off, I cannot bear to think of what this means for our country and for the Kennedy family--such pain. Jim, pour me one more, and tell me a story with a happy ending."

"Ah, I will tell you the story of my grandfather and me. I was about three years old, and we were out walking in our olive grove, a few months before we were forced to flee. This particular day was a day of celebration. It was Arbor Day, and the entire village was gathering for the party. My grandfather took me to the edge of our grove, where he had cleared a place for new trees. He carried six three-year-old saplings very tenderly, hugging their buckets to his chest. We walked, singing. I remember skipping to the newly-cleared land, where the earth was rich and dark. I asked my grandfather, 'Why do you plant new trees every year? There are more trees around here than I can count; why do we need to plant more?'

"My grandfather stretched out his arms and breathed deeply. He smiled broadly and said sweetly, 'Mohammed, my boy, I plant new trees every year for you and your children. My grandfather planted trees for me, and I hope and pray you will plant many for your grandchildren.'"

"Damn you, Mohammed Jim, I wanted to hear a story with a happy ending! You and I both had to flee from our homes and olive groves; what's happy about that?"

"Ah, Khaled, the story is still unfolding. The trees that have been planted are deeply rooted in a land that we call holy. They bear a lot of fruit, for the olives nourish many. The trees clean the air and give shade to all creatures and creation. Surely that is good news, don't you think?"

Khaled sighed and shook his head sorrowfully. "Mohammed Jim, you speak of hope in spite of dire circumstances. I don't see any silver lining, but if you believe that's a good story, I'll take it to bed and sleep on it. Goodnight, my new friend, no doubt I will see you again."

Chapter 4:

Brother Harold

The Diab family settled into their lakefront home as if they had been born to it. Khaled woke before dawn and ground dark Turkish coffee beans into a powder. As the coffee brewed, he muttered his morning chant: *"Noshkr Allah!* Thanks be to God! *Noshkr Allah!* Thanks be to God!"

By the time the pungent aroma filled the kitchen, the sun's rays were faintly visible on the horizon and glittered like stars on top of Lake Conway. Khaled poured a large cup and unobtrusively slipped out the French doors. Slowly, he walked through his fruit grove to the lakeshore, where he stood in silence and watched the sun complete her morning ascent. Mary's doctor, and his new good friend, occupied the lone boat a few miles out. His thoughts swirled with anxiety, for in a few hours, Jake Hunter was meeting him as a friend and as Mary's doctor at the Langford Hotel for Saturday brunch.

Khaled finished his coffee and slowly paced through his backyard grove, now filled to capacity with citrus, mango, papaya, peach, pear, and apple trees. His head ached with dark thoughts of the daily news; the carnage continued in Vietnam, despite a signed peace agreement with North and South Vietnam, and the United States. He mourned over the seven men who had been tried and convicted in the burglary at the Democratic Party headquarters in the Watergate Hotel, and he wondered about Nixon. After he drained his cup of coffee, he muttered aloud, "Ah, worse than any of these problems is my heartache over my homeland and my people. Fatah guerillas have taken over the Palestinian Liberation Organization now, and Yassir Arafat is supreme commander of the military arm of the PLO. This is too much power for any one man. Power always corrupts, and absolute power corrupts absolutely. Terrorism is rampant and escalating out of control. Where is the voice of reason? Where are the voices demanding justice? The atrocious attacks by my misguided brethren, the TWA and Swiss Air hijackings--what are they thinking! Yes yes yes, I know, they wanted to get the world's attention. They got it. But instead of helping their cause, they've only made people mad at them. Where are the voices of reason? Three years ago, when King Hussein demanded they leave Jordan, I didn't blame him; no one should tolerate terrorism. But, now, look at the chaos that has resulted. It is even worse now for innocent Palestinians than ever before: civil war, thousands of deaths, increasing hijackings, Palestinian Black September terrorists assassinating Prime Minister Wasfi Tal of Jordan in Cairo!

"Then, the horror of terrorists who dare claim to be Muslims, murdering eleven Israeli athletes at the Munich Olympics--my God, these men, who have given up hope, have now enlisted the Russian-trained Carlos, the Jackal. I shudder to imagine what may follow.

"Ah, it is loss of hope that makes one turn to violence and hate. We must look at the root of the problem, and work from there. God, I see it as injustice. All sides have been unjust, but it is always the innocent people who suffer the consequences of the decisions of their leaders in which they have no voice. Injustice breeds despair; despair breeds hate; and hate breeds violence.

"Oh God, I pray I am hearing you correctly. I must follow through with my plan to facilitate communications among all the Arab nations and the entire world. The Arab leadership is in such disarray; no one has modern communication technology. Imagine when they are able to pick up a phone and discuss things as if they were all in the same room! Why, if they start talking and listening to each other, imagine--"

"Daddy, Daddy," called Ahmeena from the porch, while Mary waved.

"Khaled, it's nine o'clock. Have you been out there all morning?"

"Indeed, I have. I must shower and be at the Langford by eleven o'clock. Ahmeena dear, what is your plan today?"

"Oh, Daddy, you know perfectly well that Mama and I are going to Disney with Mrs. Hunter and Katherine."

Khaled was momentarily sad as he thought, "My God, where has the time gone? She was a little kid when we moved here, and now, behold, she reminds me of my sister Fatima at fifteen. I remember, as if it were only yesterday, hugging my sister at the Tel Aviv airport, but it has been ten years already."

Khaled arrived at the Langford ten minutes late, and Dr. Jake Hunter was tapping his fingers as if playing an imaginary piano when Khaled interrupted his reverie. "Thank you, Jake, for this personal time. I know this is highly unusual, and I appreciate you speaking to me without Mary."

"Well, it is only because she insisted that we meet and discuss her condition. And besides, I've got to eat. Terese will keep an eye on Mary today; don't worry. Mary understands not to push herself, to pay attention to how she is feeling, and to sit and rest before the shortness of breath occurs. Terese and Kat can't get enough of Disney. But my one visit will last me my lifetime. Too many people--I need open spaces on my time off from work. By the way, I had a great morning on the lake; those bass were schooling on top and hitting everywhere. It was great! I love Saturdays. After we eat, I am heading off to fill deer feeders with Brother Harold out at Christmas Creek."

"Is he really your brother? I thought all your brothers were still in Memphis."

"My blood brothers are in Memphis. Harold's a good old boy and a dear friend. He looks like a blonde grizzly bear with a slight limp. He practically built my entire house. He is a master carpenter and jack-of-all-trades. His sons and mine have been hunting and fishing together for years. I've never figured out why his wife left him. He drinks a little, but I have never seen him drunk. He has a heart of gold and always lends a helping hand to anyone. As for me, I am the maverick of my family; I cannot stand to be cooped up. I need to live where I can always hunt or fish, depending on the season. My vocation is doctoring, but my passion is nature."

The waitress appeared with coffee and took their orders. Then Jake fixed his piercing blue eyes on Khaled and asked, "Ready?" Khaled nodded but trembled inside.

"Well, Khaled, as you know, Mary has had sarcoidosis for at least ten years. Her recent complaints of increasing shortness of breath, palpitations, fatigue, night sweats, and hot flashes have been thoroughly investigated via chest x-ray, EKG, and complete blood analysis. The twenty-four hour Holter monitor report has been fully evaluated, and there is no doubt. The sarcoid plaques have invaded her myocardial tissue. In other words, her heart has been affected. I am increasing her Prednisone and starting her on Digoxin and Inderal.

"As you know, the Prednisone should help reduce the inflammatory process. But with its host of adverse side effects, I only increase the dose according to the severity of symptoms, and always aim to taper it down as soon as possible. The Digoxin and Inderal will help stabilize her irregular heart rhythm. She also is going through menopause, and we can treat that with hormone therapy. The night sweats and hot flashes we can pretty much fix. The sarcoidosis prognosis is unstable at this time.

"Khaled, I am sorry I cannot be more specific than that. Mary has a serious condition, and we are doing all that we currently can. Medicine changes rapidly, so who know what the future will bring?"

"Ah, Jake, I appreciate your forthrightness. I wish it were better news. I am in anguish over following through with my decision. I gave notice to Martin Marietta two months ago, but they still do not have a replacement for my position as director of information sciences and product development. They want me to stay. With this news of Mary, I am tempted to remain, although I have managed to get everything in place for my mission. Jake, as my friend, not as Mary's doctor, what would you recommend?"

"Man, I can't advise you about what to do. All I can do is speak from my experience. Mary's condition is not good. I have known you for what--five years now? You never shut up about Majd Al Krum and your people. You have a passion and a mission. You are the only one who can make your decision."

No sooner had Jake finished speaking, than their waitress returned with steaming plates of southern cooking. Jake devoured his with gusto, while Khaled sat in silence and allowed his to grow cold. As soon as Jake finished eating, he looked at Khaled's plate and uttered, "Man, you have a problem. I have never seen you not eat your food. I wish I had better things to tell you. I am sorry to be a messenger of such gloom. Nobody can predict the future, and the course of any illness depends on many factors. You know how independently minded Mary is. If she thought you changed your plans just because of her--"

Khaled interrupted. "Believe me, I know what she will say. 'Go Khaled, go. It is your dream, your destiny.'"

"I guess you have your answer then. Look, talk to her tonight, and call my office Monday morning for a conference appointment. I will go over everything again with you and Mary, but right now I have got to head on out to the ranch. Lots of hungry deer need to be fattened up. I'll see you next week in the office, Khaled." And with that, the energetic internist rose, turned, and strode out of the Langford, while Khaled remained and brooded.

After Monday's office visit, Mary relentlessly insisted during the entire drive home, "Khaled, I will not allow any discussion of you not following through with your mission. Everything is in place. You have the best minds in the United States returning to the Middle East to help their people. You have been working tirelessly on this for over a year. How can you even consider that I wouldn't want you to go! You must do what you are being called to.

"Khaled, I love you dearly and will miss you severely. When Ahmeena graduates middle school in six weeks, we will join you in Cairo. I am in good hands with Dr. Hunter; the new medication will work wonders. Do not fret, and do not get cold feet. I insist on driving you to the airport tomorrow night, and we will hug farewell. But it will only be for a short while. Ahmeena and I will join you during school break, and you will see--I will be much better then!"

Khaled felt a sense of peace that he had not known since before Saturday's brunch. "Mary, how could I ever refuse you? You are right. There is no need to worry. Everything will be alright. You are right again that everything I have been working towards these many years has finally come to light. The nine best Arab engineers and communications specialists are totally committed to spending the next year in the Middle East. In just a few days, my team and I will be traveling to all the Arab nations to begin the educational phase of our mass communication enterprise that we are bringing to the Arab world. I just had a flash; we will name our organization the AT&T of the Middle East."

Jake and Harold had finished filling seven deer feeders scattered throughout their privately-held four thousand acres of wetland an hour east of Orlando, on the outskirts of the rural town of Christmas. The two men were in partnership with a group of professional businessmen, who had purchased the undeveloped acreage as an investment. Jake, Harold, and a few other partners also used the property as a hunting preserve.

While riding in a dilapidated camouflaged Jeep on the way back to camp, Harold yelled, "Hey, look! There are two deer in the clearing--nice fat does." Jake cut the engine and the men sat in silence, watching the deer graze. Out of the thick palmettos, a twelve-point and a young buck with peach-fuzzed antlers appeared. The men watched in awe as the deer fed. When the majestic stag raised his eyes to the men and snorted, they all turned and bolted.

Further down the dirt road, Harold yelled once again, "Look, I think there is another herd way over there."

Jake focused his cerulean eyes where Harold pointed and wryly retorted, "Harold, that's a bunch of hogs!"

"Oh, guess my eyes aren't what they use to be." Harold pulled out a purple velveteen sack that enrobed his bottle of Crown Royal and asked, "Care for some sustenance, Jake?"

Jake shook his head as he lit a cigar and grabbed a Tab from the cooler at his side. "You know, Brother Harold, I cannot get my neighbor's problem off my mind. It's usually my patients that keep me awake. But all day, I keep seeing this poor guy's face. He's worried about his wife, and there is cause for concern. If that weren't enough, he's on this mission to help save the world. I've told you about all of that, remember?"

Harold snorted affirmatively, and Jake continued, "Dr. D. has more passion and commitment to social justice issues than anyone I have ever personally known. He is flying to Cairo Tuesday night, and I just told him his wife's condition is unstable. For the past year, he has been working out a deal with the president of the Arab Fund for Social and Economic Development in Kuwait. He did this while working fifty hours a week at Martin Marietta. He has this incredible vision of linking the twenty-two Arab countries via modern telecommunication systems. He rounded up nine Arab-Americans with advanced degrees and lucrative positions to quit their jobs, go back to their homeland, and help their people. This Dr. D. is an incredible person. He's a Muslim, but he's a better Christian than a lot of Christians I've known."

"Yeah, man, I know exactly what you mean. But what I just don't get is why those people over there keep fighting each other. If they are all so religious, why don't they do what their religions teach and treat each other the way they want to be treated?"

Jake eased naturally into his other role of teacher and lecturer, and launched into a history lesson. "This modern conflict between Palestinian Arabs and Jews began around the turn of the twentieth century. The two groups have different religions; do you understand that 'Palestinian' means Muslims, Christians, and Druze? The animosity towards Israel is not about religious differences, but about land. The UN divided the area known as Palestine into three parts in 1947: Israel, the West Bank, and the Gaza Strip. This is a very small geographical area, about the size of Maryland.

"Imagine carving up the state of Maryland, forcing the folks out of their homes without paying them, and ripping up their deeds. It really is an unjust situation, and things are more out of hand all the time. This morning, when we were discussing if he should go or not, I had a sense of uneasiness that had nothing to do with doctoring. Something I can't put my finger on, like a bad premonition--but now I am sounding like my wife!"

Brother Harold nodded and rubbed his protuberant abdomen before responding. "Well, you don't have to be a psychic to know bad stuff will keep on happening over there. What's the deal with the UN? Why can't they maintain peace there?"

"Well, the United Nations was the body that carved up the borders, and that is what led to the 1948 war. In November of 1947, even though the Arab Nations disagreed with the boundary lines, the UN went ahead with their plan. You see, after the fall of the Turkish Ottoman Empire, Britain had taken control of the land via a mandate whose time had run out. With Britain withdrawing from the area, the Jewish people flooded the region, claiming not just the territory given to them by the UN, but also places like Dr. D's hometown. It was Palestinian territory, according to the UN.

"Imagine the outrage, and you can understand why the Arab nations that surround the area formerly known as Palestine attacked the new state of Israel. That was the war of 1948. Since then, there have been two more wars, in '56 and '67, and I won't be surprised when another happens. Understand, these attackers are being born and bred in the refugee camps. Imagine being young and healthy, and having no prospects or future. There is not much else to do but make babies. And they most certainly have been busy doing that. The Palestinians no longer have a nation, so they cannot get passports to migrate elsewhere.

"The group known as *Fedayeen*, which means 'self-sacrificer,' was born in the despair of the refugee camps. These men have given up hope of returning to their homes, which mostly have been torn down and rebuilt by the Israelis now. These *Fedayeen* do not only sacrifice themselves; they kill innocent people. This naturally causes retaliation, which sets into place the continuing cycle of violence and destruction."

"So why exactly does your friend want to go back over there?"

"He is a man with a vision and a passion. He is committed to justice for both sides, and he believes he can make a positive difference. If you knew him personally, Harold, you would believe it, too."

Harold lifted his almost empty pouch of Crown Royal and exclaimed, "Let's toast the man, and then I'll tell you what my daddy told me when I was a kid, when my brothers and I would get out of hand. He'd say, 'boys, you all are going the way of Cain and Abel, and you'd better quit. For one of those boys was filled with so much hatred and jealousy that he killed the other.' Then my old man would be on a roll, and he'd tell us about Sarah, Abraham's wife. And we loved to hear that part, so we'd quit our fight. You see, although Sarah had already reached menopause, she still desired a child. God had even shared a laugh with her about it coming true, but just like a woman, she took the matter into her own hands, and refused to wait for the Lord to deliver. So old Sarah decided to give her maidservant to her old man, and that chick and Abraham made a kid. Everything was fine when Ishmael arrived, but only for a very short while.

"Now, although Sarah was a dried-up old crone, she, too, birthed a son, and named him after the laughter she had shared with God, but called the kid Isaac. Sarah had gotten very territorial and demanded Abraham cast out his beloved first son with his mama Haggar, into the barren wilderness, and Abraham did it! But, as God always hears the cries of mothers and sons, he promised to make a great nation from Ishmael's descendants, too. And thus, the Arab nation was born.

"By the sixth century before Christ, the conflicts in the land were already old news, and Jeremiah warned the people that all God could see was violence and destruction in the city. Sickness and wounds were all around. And then my old man would get tears in his eyes and softly recite, 'for every misunderstanding, every condemning thought, every negative vibration, every tear torn from a heart, every time one grabbed and wouldn't let go, and they only did it because they did not know. The Divine is within all creation and within all women and men. And every tiny kindness you have ever done, every gentle word spoken, every time you held your tongue, every positive thought, every smile freely given, every helping hand that opens, helps bring in the kingdom. And the kingdom comes from above, and it comes from within. Imagine a kingdom of sisterhood of all creatures and all men.'"

Harold stroked a tear away with the velvet pouch that held his Crown Royal, drew the last swig and offered up, "Godspeed to Dr. D on his mission from God."

Back at the Langford Hotel, Khaled sat on the barstool and lifted a glass of iced tea with Mohammed Jim. "My friend, tonight will be the last time we will speak for a while. I plan to be gone for as long as it takes to do this job that has been set before me. The first night we met, five years ago, you told me a story about you and your grandfather. It has remained with me, and I have often remembered it as I walked through my fruit orchard. Your grandfather was a wise man. This thought occurred to me the other morning as I remembered your story. I will make time to visit your village of Al Birah and plant an olive tree there, in honor of you and your family's roots. Your grandfather understood that roots from the past connect to the future. I salute his wisdom."

Mohammed Jim lifted his tea in a toast and proclaimed, "Khaled, I salute you and your plan, and pray for your safety."

CHAPTER 5:

YOU CAN GO HOME AGAIN

ON THE PLANE TO Cairo, Khaled was oblivious to the fluent Arabic of the nine companions who surrounded him. He kept his eyes shut, and in his mind, he was once again back in 1963, receiving his American citizenship and the passport that allowed him to return to Majd Al Krum for the first time since he had fled in 1948. He clearly saw, once more, the Ben Guerin Tel Aviv Airport surrounded by the fertile green expanse below and the azure sky that embraced him with a sense of the presence of God. He audibly growled at the intrusive memory of how swiftly the other disembarked passengers were led through customs, while he was informed by the agent, "Sir, come with me to the interrogation room."

It was as if he was again being led down the long corridor to the closet-sized room with the man with eyes so blue they startled him. He shivered as he once again heard the Russian demanding, "Why are you making this trip here, and where will you be going?"

"Sir, I am an American citizen. I have an American passport. I was born in Majd Al Krum. I have returned to visit my family, who I have not seen since 1948. My brother is meeting me here, and we will go directly to my home, three hours away. I will stay for two weeks, then return to my new home in the United States, back to my wife and child. I left Majd Al Krum in 1948; I have never been allowed to return to my home and see my family until now! I just received my American passport and citizenship, and want to visit my family and home!"

"And why did you leave in the first place?"

"Sir, you are older than I. You surely remember why."

"Why do you say you left?"

"Sir, I left for fear of my life."

"Well, if you have nothing to hide, you should have no fear."

Khaled had no time to react, for another door opened into the room, and Khaled's suitcase was brought in. It was silently dismantled and thoroughly examined by the blue-eyed interrogator, as the deliveryman hovered menacingly.

"Very good for you. Now, step this way for your full body exam by Mr. Sharon."

Khaled bit his lip until it bled and trembled, for the name Sharon evoked a painful memory. Khaled knew all about Unit 101, a special IDF commando group commanded by Ariel Sharon. Some Palestinians, who had given up hope of ever returning home, had lobbed a grenade into a house in the Israeli settlement of Yehud. There was the senseless murder of an Israeli woman and two children. In retaliation, Unit 101 struck the Palestinian village of Qibya, killing sixty innocent people. One of them had been Khaled's roommate at Jerusalem College. Khaled was sweating profusely as he numbly followed Mr. Sharon into another closet-sized room.

"Remove your jacket and raise your arms," Mr. Sharon commanded, and Khaled felt ill. He trembled as he undressed, humiliated and angry at the same time. He held his breath and kept so silent he could hear the beating of his own heart, as he was thoroughly patted down. Then Mr. Sharon turned his attention to Khaled's jacket, pulled every pocket inside out.

When he was satisfied, he led Khaled back out, nodded to his coworker, and left. Khaled was mortified and nauseated, and filled with inner rage, but remained calm and silent, and listened intently to his blue-eyed interrogator. "There are hundreds of Palestinians outside the terminal. We do not yet know why they have gathered, and we can take no chances, you understand? You must tell me everything that has happened to you since you left Majd Al Krum."

Khaled was almost ecstatic over the opportunity to tell his interrogator, "From 1948 until 1953, I lived in Syria and taught mathematics to high school children. I left for America in 1953; I have worked very hard, and I received a Ph.D. in engineering. I have been employed by the Westinghouse Company. I have an American-born wife and child at home in Buffalo, New York, and I intend to see them again in two weeks."

"Mr. Diab, my name is Mr. Kazmeroski. Tell me, what do you do at the Westinghouse Company, Mr. Diab?"

Khaled was jolted, as this was the first time he had been addressed by name. "I am in defense programs." Khaled spoke firmly, then bit his lip again.

"What do you do in defense programs?" Mr. Kazmeroski inquired, and Khaled noted that his eyes seemed to have changed to a warm blue that reminded him of the sky on an Iowa spring day.

"I am the senior scientist and head of research, in charge of engineering certain aspects of the United States' defense programs that are designed to defend the United States and her allies in case of enemy attack. My projects are for protection against enemy attack. I have top-secret clearance on the Minute Man missiles and anti-jam communications systems. I have told you more than I should. I am worn out. I am no threat. I am a law-abiding citizen, a hard worker, and a husband and father. I came back home to see my family. Please, won't you let me go?"

"Mr. Diab, I apologize for any inconvenience. I will summon a taxi for you, and you will be on your way."

Khaled sighed deeply. "Thanks, but my brother is supposed to meet me, and we will drive directly to Majd Al Krum. I am most grateful to be on my way. Tell me, sir, do you love this country?"

Mr. Kazmeroski boomed, "Of course I do!"

Khaled spoke quietly. "I love it more than you can ever know, for it is my homeland."

Mr. Kazmeroski's blue eyes filled with tears that then overflowed. "My God, of course, I understand. I love my Russian motherland, too! I apologize for such a thorough exam, but you understand that it is my job."

Khaled sighed deeply and responded, "I just want to go home again."

Mr. Kazmeroski stood and asked, "May I accompany you out and make sure you have that ride to take you home?"

Khaled nodded and followed Mr. Kazmeroski to the exit doors, where a congregation of Palestinians in native garb had gathered and were waving excitedly and chanting "*Marhaba, Marhaba!*"

Mr. Kazmeroski spoke. "These people arrived hours ago, they--" He trailed off as he noticed Khaled's face, which registered shock and awe.

"My God, I cannot believe it; the whole village of Majd Al Krum has turned out!" Buckets of tears flowed as Khaled's father and mother surged forth. The three embraced and cried with joy, while the crowd erupted in cheers. Mr. Kazmeroski stood, transfixed, at the doorway of the terminal, for never had he witnessed such a homecoming. After everyone had been embraced and greeted, Khaled was confronted by a young girl, who began kissing and hugging him more than any other.

"My dear girl, I am overwhelmed by this entire reception already, but you are hugging and kissing me more than my own mother! Please stop kissing and hugging me already; I do not even know who you are."

"Do you not know who I am?" she implored.

"I see a beautiful young girl before me, who I have never seen before."

"But you have seen me; you even held me in your arms. I am your sister, Fatima; I was one month old when you left home."

Khaled was overwhelmed with deep emotion, then embraced and kissed his little sister. "Fatima, I pledge to you that I will never let so much time pass before visiting you again!"

Khaled's father patted his back and spoke. "Khaled, I am so very proud of you. Let us all return to Majd Al Krum and celebrate, for my son has come home."

It was well past dark when the entourage drove between the Mediterranean Sea and olive-tree-covered mountains. Khaled sat in the back seat, in between his mother and sister, as his father drove and bombarded Khaled with questions.

"Son, what made you want to become an American the most?"

"America is a land of justice for all people. That is what the US Constitution and the Declaration of Independence say, and they are the foundation of American ways. They promise that all men, of every color and every race, are guaranteed the inalienable rights of life, liberty, and the pursuit of happiness! They guarantee justice and freedom for all the people who are citizens. As much as I love my homeland beyond words, I also love my new land and am grateful to be a part of it. How I wish that what America guarantees its citizens would be true for all the people of the Holy Land, and the entire world, too!"

A flashing red light accosted the car, and a loud "HALT!" was heard. A Jordanian officer with a flashlight approached and demanded, "Where are you going?"

"Home to Majd Al Krum, but I think we missed our turn," Mr. Diab, Sr., intoned.

"You have, indeed; turn around here. You have traveled eight kilometers too far."

By the time Khaled and his family returned home, their house was brightly lit, and food was being served. It was thirty hours before Khaled laid down under an olive tree and fell asleep, yet the party continued the entire two weeks that Khaled was home. On the third day, Riad arrived from Cairo, and he and Khaled spent hours together under the shade of a massive olive tree. It was hours before Riad turned serious and unburdened his heart.

"Oh, Khaled, as exciting as my work assisting in the translating of the Nag Hammadi library is, I must share some grief with you. I do not speak of my despair to anyone else, and it is heavy on my heart to share. I was in Beirut on a holiday a few weeks ago. Well, there I was at the Hotel Imperial, enjoying myself, but knowing that just around the corner is the Shatilla refugee camp.

I resisted until my last morning in Beirut to take a walk and visit there. I was shocked by how many more people now live there. The tents have been replaced with thin metal chicken coops!

"What is wrong with the world, when people who once had homes are forced to live in chicken coops? It was better when they had tents. They were temporary, and all could believe they would be going home soon. The United Nations and Lebanese government provided the refugees with chicken coop materials, and the refugees made their own shelters. As I approached, a gang of children jumped and yelled '*Marhaba, Marhaba!*' I was relieved to see that they seemed happy, and then two Palestinian men joined us and asked if I was the new relief worker. They told me their water supply was drying up. Many children were dying of thirst. They asked if I brought water.

"Khaled, I was devastated; what could I do? Why had not the UN or Lebanese government provided them with adequate water and better conditions? I fear it is the same old tale, told all through history: there is corruption in high places, and the little people are ignored. A man named Ziad invited me to follow him, and then the entire camp gathered around us. They were glad for some company, but no doubt disappointed I was not an aid worker with water and food. Ziad told me that most everyone still believed that if they stayed firm and remained together in the refugee camps, the world would demand they be given their rights, and they would all return to their homelands, or be compensated. Khaled, I had no heart to tell them that many of their leaders have become rich from oil and do not care that children are born and die in refugee camps. I could not tell them that their family homes and groves have disappeared. So many children were sick, and so many old people were in pain.

"Khaled, I cannot bear the images I saw. Yet, Ziad was able to make light of such distress. He showed me his small space that he shared with a wife and five children. He pointed out a hole in the ceiling and joked, 'See that hole? It is good for air in the dry season, and when the rains come, we all get to take showers.'"

Khaled wiped a tear from his eyes and said, "Riad, what more can I do? I will continue to sponsor as many young men from Shatilla as I can afford, but with a young daughter, I must also provide a future with hope for her. I can only do so much. I must believe God has a reason for our pain and suffering. We cannot understand God's mind, but it is all we can hope for--that he has a plan and a reason for this."

Riad responded vehemently. "There is no reason on earth or in heaven that people should suffer so. There are enough resources and wealth in the world to remedy this injustice."

The men fell silent for a long while. Both stared up into the gnarly branches of the ageless olive tree. Khaled was the first to speak. "I will not rest until justice has been served. There must be a way my people can go home. There must be hope; there must be healing. There must be something I can do. I will have to think about it; I will spend time imagining something. Something will come to me--something that all people of good will can also do to help. But I have no clue what that may be right now."

Riad sighed deeply and told him, "Khaled, remember three things. First is my favorite Rilke: 'You must give birth to your images. They are the future waiting to be born. Fear not the strangeness you feel. The future must enter you long before it happens.' And second, remember what Gandhi said: 'Be the change you want to see in the world.' And never forget what Pope Paul VI said: 'if you want peace, you must work for justice.'"

CHAPTER 6:

ROOTS OF WISDOM

IN THE MEETING ROOM, while waiting for the nine men to return from lunch and continue their monthly meeting, Khaled shouted, "No!" He banged both of his fists on top of the massive rectangular conference table.

The Cairo radio again announced, "A surprise attack this morning by Egyptian and Syrian forces has proven to be a triumph of military superiority! Just twelve hours ago, eighty thousand Egyptian soldiers began marching across the Suez Canal and have traveled fifteen miles inland. Again, today, Saturday, October 6, 1973, Egyptian and Syrian troops have overwhelmed the Israelis. Today is a triumph for the Arab nations and a great day in history! Syrian troops now occupy the Golan Heights in northern Israel. We are grateful for the assistance of Iraq, Saudi Arabia, Kuwait, Libya, Tunisia, Sudan, Morocco, and Jordan."

Khaled shut the radio off and felt nauseated. "What are my misguided brethren thinking, attacking on the holiest day of prayer and fasting in the Jewish calendar? I can imagine how devastating this Yom Kippur news will be to my friend Art. He must be thinking there is another holocaust!

"God have mercy on my brethren; I repent for them. But they also make me livid! For the past six months, my team and I have been knocking ourselves out, trying to educate twenty-two Arab governments about networking communications between themselves and the entire world.

"They do not want to hear outside opinions that differ from their own. They do not care about helping the poor and oppressed people who fill their countries or are packed into refugee camps. They do not see how a mass communication network would stimulate the economies of their countries. The poor people could be trained easily to do the manufacturing with machines. The youth would have a future with hope. They would have employment and the dignity that honest labor brings. All these ministers of communications ask is 'What's in it for me?'

"Every report I have read today sounds the same--only the names change. Greed and avarice fill the government positions. It's all about the money or power. They have lost touch with the common man. They do not care about the poor people living in such poverty all around them. My heart breaks. My team and I have given up a lot in America to offer change, opportunity, and hope. But so much of the leadership here is corrupt.

"For twenty-five years now, Palestinians have been kept in refugee camps. Their homes are gone, and they have never received compensation. My hope was to stimulate the Arab economies with the manufacturing of phones, and that all the jobs that would generate would bring opportunity to the poor, who have for so long been ignored. There would be work for the youth I see hanging out around the camps with nothing to do. It breaks my heart. They must have a future with gainful work and honest labor, and receive honest wages."

Khaled re-experienced the electrical shock that had run through him, as he recalled the very day Mary and Ahmeena flew back to Orlando after their one-week vacation in Cairo with him in July. No sooner had their plane disappeared, than a squadron of Iraqi hunter jet fighters flew overhead. He muttered aloud, "Now I understand; they used those jet fighters today on Yom Kippur. Why is it so easy for leadership to communicate for destruction, yet never listen to the voice of wisdom and reason, the voice demanding justice and peace?"

Just then, the somber nine members of the AT&T of the Middle East mission silently filed into the Hotel Imperial's conference room for their monthly meeting. Each nodded to Khaled on their way to their seats, but he did not see them. The group sat in silence, until a beefy man with white hair and a beard quietly shifted in his chair, and then stood.

"Brothers." Ibrahim spoke softly. "We all have heard the bad news of more war. Even though the sounds are triumphant, we know all war brings unexpected pain. We should all pray for the people who are in leadership, and especially for those caught up in the crossfire."

After many prayers and anxieties were shared, Khaled called the meeting to order. "I thank you all for the reports you provided me this morning at breakfast. I have been in this room, reading them, all day. I wish one had a positive message. You all echo the same experience, and it is exactly what I have been experiencing myself. All the ministers of communication have been reported to be accommodating and gracious, but none have shared our vision of helping the poor and oppressed. We have offered the vision of manufacturing jobs that would provide a future with hope to the masses of poverty-stricken people who fill their lands. The idea of enabling all the people to be able to call family and friends throughout the world has been now offered to every Arab state. At this time, only two people in the Arab world, out of every one hundred, even own a phone! And for those who do, it is doubtful they ever can get a call through within two days! Now, this war on Yom Kippur is devastating news. I do not blame any of you for cutting and running, and no doubt the American Embassy may soon be telling us all to leave."

"Khaled, what are you going to do?" Ibrahim asked.

"I will stay to honor the contract I entered into with the president of the Arab Fund for Social and Economic Development in Kuwait. Cairo has been our meeting center, but I report to Kuwait, so I will travel there tomorrow to report our findings to Mr. Allaal. He is a fine man and has been so encouraging about our project. We shared high hopes. Once he sees the bill to implement our plan, he may change his mind, now, with this war. War destroys, but many opportunities to build will bring healing and growth. I am willing to persist, even though it will be tough, going against the incompetent greed we fight against. Although I am deeply disappointed by what we have discovered about the leadership of the nations, I still believe in the wisdom of mass communication."

Ibrahim said, "Khaled, everyone gathered around this table has had the opportunity to go to America, and has realized the American dream. We have seized every opportunity that came before us. We know from experience what justice and liberty provide, and that all people have value and dignity. This is the American way, and if only it were true for all people throughout the world--well, that would be paradise, I suppose. We can only do the good we see before us. Allah has blessed us with the opportunity to go to America and receive excellent educations and material wealth. It was a very good life that we all left behind.

"And now, we find ourselves caught up in the turbulence and violence of this hour. We are all free to leave as soon as we can book a flight out. But, I think about those innocent poor people who cannot leave, and all the collateral damage that war brings. Ah, forgive me. I digress. It is possible that, in spite of all of our efforts, and the great vision of bringing mass communication to the Arab world, it may not happen. We should prepare ourselves in case our mission will have to be aborted. I cannot imagine that Israel is down and out yet. They have the capability to defend themselves. They will not give up without a fight. They were caught unaware. They will retaliate, no doubt, and what will America do? We should be prepared for the US Embassy to tell us to leave. As much as I believe in this vision of mass-communication, it may not be for this time in history."

Khaled welled up, and the tears overflowed. "I have been consumed for too long by this vision of mass communication and cannot accept that it will not happen. As long as I have hope, I will continue. I have worked and believed too long not to."

The men all averted their eyes, for Khaled's passion was hard to bear. They all agreed to persist until the American Embassy advised them to leave.

Ibrahim's prophetic words came true three days later, when the Israeli forces counterattacked in the Sinai. The Israeli army managed to push back the Egyptian military and crossed the Suez Canal to within sixty-five miles of Cairo. Khaled and the president of the Arab Fund for Social and Economic Development had just finished discussing current events, when Mr. Allaal continued, "Khaled, your project will still receive funding, I assure you. I believe in the necessity of your plan. The UN will settle this crisis, and I want you to carry on, of course. Do you know that I know Anwar Sadat personally? No? I am surprised. I thought it was common knowledge. We went to school together as boys, and his wife is a cousin to my wife. He will listen to voices of wisdom about the need to make peace. I can talk to him, and he has always heeded much of my advice in the past. He did not share this plan to attack with me. No doubt he knew I would have tried to talk him out of it. But power went to his head, and he received bad advice. I will be seeing him at a wedding next week, and will give him a piece of my mind. Khaled, you must persist in this effort of mass communication. The common people will benefit greatly, and that will make for stable nations."

That was enough to fill Khaled with hope, and when he learned that the UN had organized a cease-fire agreement on October 24, he traveled with a much lighter heart. He zealously made the rounds to every minister of communication in twenty-two nations. Even after inspecting the deplorable manufacturing companies already in operation, he was confident that with retraining and retooling, his vision of mass communication would be realized.

The months stretched into two years, and Khaled's hope of reforming the incompetent and corrupt bureaucracies that comprised the communications ministries in the Arab lands finally faded. The members of the AT&T of the Middle East had deserted him months earlier. In May of 1975, he admitted defeat.

Khaled snapped his suitcase closed, and heard a knock at the door and Raid's greeting, "*Marhaba.*"

"*Marhaba*, Riad. Come in, and thank you. I am grateful for your company on my visit to the village of Al Birah. Maybe I should have taken that trip when I first arrived in Cairo. Maybe if I had gone and planted that olive tree for Mohammed Jim two years ago when I arrived, things might have worked out differently."

"Oh, Khaled, you are too hard on yourself. At this moment in time, it appears that you have not accomplished the mission you had planned. But you have made many contacts and have proven yourself to be honest and ethical, and we all can be grateful for that. Also, the news is good for a change.

"Anwar Sadat and Menachem Begin are talking to each other. Who knows? If that dialogue continues between them, peace and justice can prevail. The time for your mass communication project may be just up the road. Do not give up your vision, just because it didn't work out the way you planned. Have faith, Khaled; no effort for good is ever wasted. But I must warn you about the landscape you will see in what was formerly Palestine. All that remains of many homes is rubble, embraced by the many cacti that were planted as borders around Palestinian homes. New apartments and cities have sprung up where once were olive groves. You have not made this journey from Cairo to Jerusalem since you were a boy in college. It will look very different this time around."

The men traveled the entire day with little conversation. When they arrived in Jerusalem after dark, Khaled was shell-shocked from the differences in the landscape he had witnessed. The men walked through the narrow, winding streets of Jerusalem that were a beehive of activity, and past restaurants where people dined al fresco.

"Riad, let's get out of here; I feel uncomfortable. When I walked these streets thirty years ago, I heard just as much Arabic as Hebrew. Now I hear no Arabic spoken in all of Jerusalem. I wonder, if I were a young man now, would they even allow me to go to Jerusalem College? This town had been my home for four years, but now I am a stranger in a strange land. Let's get a taxi as fast as we can."

Riad did not have the heart to tell Khaled that Jerusalem College had become the headquarters of the UN Relief Agency, and now was controlled by the Israeli government. As they rode the twenty kilometers to the village of Al Birah, Khaled never stopped shaking, and Riad gave up trying to comfort him with words. As they reached the outskirts of Al Birah, the taxi driver asked, "Exactly where do you want to be dropped?"

Khaled quickly responded, "By the first olive grove you come to."

After stepping from the cab into the cold night air on the outskirts of the small town, Khaled announced, "Riad, I want to spend my last night in the Holy Land under the canopy of an olive tree. Do you mind if we do not stay at the village inn, but right here?"

"Khaled, it is a little cool tonight, but I can take it if you can."

"I do not even feel it. I am still numb from the trip and the changes I witnessed from the plane. So many villages that I once knew no longer exist. Stopping in Jerusalem was the last straw. I am whipped, and this olive tree is welcoming me. Let's spend the night here."

The men reminisced about family, friends, and all the parties they had attended under the shade of olive trees. Both fell asleep within seconds of each other and woke at cockcrow.

"Khaled, I am starving! Let's find the inn and get some coffee. The local nursery should open early; it's Monday. Then we'll plant your tree and catch a cab. I have to give a report in two days. It's all in my head, but I must get to my typewriter and bang it out. The time we spent in silence dredged up some new ideas."

"Riad, you have been mysteriously silent about what you are up to these days."

"Khaled, before I picked you up yesterday morning, I had been rereading the ancient Hebrew writings of Rabbi Hillel, who lived a hundred years before the Common Era. He built a bridge of understanding between Hebrew and Greek philosophy. He wrote that the Jewish idea of *Hoekma*, meaning 'holy wisdom,' and understood as feminine divinity, was the same as the Greek idea of the *Logos*, meaning the 'Word." The Christian writers Saint Paul and Saint John both echo his formulation when they wrote about Jesus being the wisdom of God. Therefore, one with an open mind can readily imagine that before Jesus was born a man, he was a woman—Holy Wisdom."[15]

Khaled interrupted. "You are reminding me of Jake Hunter. Every time I go out fishing with him, he goes on about God as Mother and how God manifests in nature, and when we are close to nature, we can hear the word in all of creation."

Riad nodded and continued. "In ancient understanding, wisdom was always understood as a form of feminine divinity. It is evident through my study of the Nag Hammadi library that many of the patriarchs did not value the wisdom of women. The gospels attributed to women were silenced by the early church fathers until just recently.

"The Gospels of Mary Magdalene and Pistis Sophia are available in modern translations now. One with eyes to see may read them and ears to hear may hear them. Khaled, your efforts for mass communication would enable many ears to hear good news of peace and reconciliation. Your plan was noble and your heart was pure, but the mystery we call God works through people. And we are all imperfect vessels. The journey you have taken this far is all part of the divine plan. During our travels, I kept hearing the voice of wisdom as recorded in the Old Testament, Proverbs 8: 'Listen! Wisdom is calling...What I say is true...To those with insight it is all clear; I am Wisdom...whoever looks for me can find me...I follow the paths of justice.'[16]

"Khaled, follow the path of justice that has been set before you. Your path will take you across many bridges and many nations. Go the way of wisdom."

Khaled did not have the heart to tell Riad he had no clue about what he was alluding to. Khaled just nodded his head, and Riad serenely smiled. The men walked in silence, until they both inhaled the aroma of strong coffee brewing, and Riad offered, "Khaled, let's knock at this door, and see if we can't receive a cup of java."

A bent old man opened the door slightly, and introductions on all sides were exchanged. Then Khaled said, "I have come to plant an olive tree for my friend who once lived in this village. His name is Mohammed Lama."

The old man staggered against the door, and tears fell down his cheeks. He shook as he spoke. "That is my nephew!"

"*Noshkr Allah!* Thanks be to God. He said he still had some family here, but I never expected to find any. I have come here to plant an olive tree in his honor. He is a good friend, and although I have not seen him in two years, I received a letter from him just a few months ago. He graduated with honors in pre-law at Rollins College in Winter Park, and is now at the University of Florida, in Gainesville, finishing his degree."

The old man had regained his composure, opened the door of his modest home fully, and bellowed, "Welcome, my friends, *Noshkr Allah*, indeed. The gift of your presence is gratefully received. Please join us for breakfast. I will escort you to our fine local tree nursery after you share a meal with my wife and me. My uncle owns the tree nursery two kilometers from here, and my truck is dependable. My uncle and I refused to leave in '48, but we sent all the young people to Lebanon. None have ever returned. The last news I had was that Mohammed was living in the Shatilla refugee camp. You bring the best news I have had in a very long time, gentlemen."

Mrs. Lama happily prepared a feast, and the men had their fill and then some. After returning from the local nursery where they had been welcomed like royalty, Mr. Lama drove them to the western corner of his olive grove. "Once we walk through these old trees, there is a small pond where an ancient olive tree had stood for centuries. It finally died last year, and we chopped it down and sold its trunk to the local craftsmen. They are transforming it into furniture and art. I had just finished clearing the land and tilling the soil three days ago for replanting, and that is where we are heading."

Each of the three men carried a three-gallon bucket containing a three-year-old sapling. When they reached the edge of the grove and first set eyes on the pool of water sparkling in the early morning sun, Khaled froze in place and remarked, "Ah, this is beautiful."

The men took turns with the only shovel to dig a hole in the rich, dark brown humus of the Holy Land. Together, they placed the sapling into the center of the hole, gently wrapped the fertile soil around the roots, patted it tightly, and watered the plants from the jug Mr. Lama toted on his head.

Mr. Lama spoke first after the planting. "My new friends, I dedicate this olive tree to you and your kin, and thank Allah for his mercy and compassion, which embraces all things. May the roots grow deep and may it bear a lot of fruit."

Then Khaled offered, "I keep hearing the voice of my good friend and neighbor Jake quoting Dorothy Day. Now I truly understand it: 'God is everywhere, but under the trees and looking over any wide expanse of water, he communicates himself to me and fills me with a deep quiet peace.'"[17]

Riad smiled broadly and squinted in the sunlight. "Gentlemen, you have both spoken with the voice of wisdom."

CHAPTER 7:

A CAT NAMED CHESTER

KHALED DEPLANED INTO THE rapidly evolving McCoy Airport in Orlando, and once more felt like a stranger in his own homeland. Scores of young, exhausted families with Mickey Mouse ears filled the holding area of the terminal where he disembarked. He anxiously made his way to baggage claim, all the while searching every passing face. When he lifted his luggage and walked towards the exit, he began to worry. He had spoken with Mary less than thirty hours ago, and expected her and Ahmeena to meet him when he deplaned.

He knew Ahmeena had been driving Mary all around town for the past six months without one incident. He shoved away the thought of an accident and whispered, "I am not going to get myself all upset, just because they are running late. This crowd of humanity, coming and going--a lot of changes have occurred in Orlando in just two years. It is the season of afternoon pop-up storms, and my daughter will drive more slowly. I refuse to worry."

He exited the terminal and was hit with a blast of hot, wet air, as if an overheated oven had just opened in his face. Sweat poured down his brow and caused his eyes to burn. Not until Mrs. Hunter was shouting up at him, did he even notice her.

"Khaled, welcome home; Mary and Ahmeena are fine. Well, not perfectly fine, but nothing that you need to get anxious about. I only just got here; I'm sorry to be late. Let me grab one of these bags, and I'll fill you in as we walk to my wheels."

"Terese, start talking about where Mary and Ahmeena are right now."

"Okay, they are at home. Mary fell this morning and broke her wrist. When she opened the door to let Chester out, he tripped her up, and she fell. Ahmeena hadn't left yet for school and called me. I piled them into the car and flew to Jake's office. He did an x-ray and sent us to the Jewitt clinic. Dr. Mac put on a cast from her fingers to her upper arm. I just dropped them back at home, and that is why I am late."

Khaled sighed with relief. "I feel horrible that Mary has suffered again, and I was not there for her! She knows that when Chester sees those citrus rats scurrying up the oak tree, he cannot be held back. Chester sees a moving object and bolts like a stallion at the starting gate. Well, what else has been going on since I saw Mary and Ahmeena off at the Cairo Airport after their final visit before I threw in the towel on Middle East communications?"

Terese responded in her clipped, rapid delivery. "Ok, well, I picked them up that day when they returned home. When Mary got in the car, she told me she had been aware of a fluttering feeling in her chest; it had started the morning she flew home. She didn't mention it to you, because she thought it would go away. She thought it was the usual pre-flight jitters and wasn't worried a bit when you two said goodbye in Cairo. Unfortunately, it continued on and increased all during her flight. As soon as she told me this, I did a one-eighty and zoomed over to Jake's office. He did an EKG and said she was in rapid atrial fibrillation. He admitted her to Winter Park Hospital for three days.

"Don't blow your top. Mary insisted we not call you. She was adamant, and you know I am not going to cross her, and neither will Jake. So, Jake adjusted her medicines; she got better and had been fine until this morning when she fell. She is resting at home, and Ahmeena is always happy to be with her. You have an incredible kid; you both should be very proud. Jake said he is fishing early tomorrow morning on Lake Conway. He said to tie your white handkerchief to your wrist just before dawn if you want to go fishing tomorrow morning, and he will pick you up and answer all your questions."

Khaled kept closemouthed as he thought, God, I give up! I surrender. I gave my heart and sweat to the vision of mass communication in the Middle East, and it did not happen. I accept it was not your will or not your time for it. But now, I have just gotten home and to find out my Mary has been in the hospital twice, and I wasn't there for her. Oh God, I feel like a failure. How can I ever make it up to her? She means more to me than anything, and I pray to you, God, to please protect her.

Terese drove in silence, and had parked in the Diab driveway and deposited the luggage at the front doorstep before Khaled came out of his trance. As he exited the car and began thanking her for the ride, the front door opened wide, and there stood Mary.

Khaled gasped, for an enormous, reddish-blue bruise crept all the way up her neck to her jaw; he exclaimed, "Mary, I want to hug you, but I am afraid you will break."

Mary laughed and embraced Khaled, while Mrs. Hunter delivered the bags to the master room. Terese was pleased that they never even noticed her departure, for their hug continued long after she had pulled out of the driveway.

Ahmeena was waiting at the olivewood table, looking out into the orchard and the wide expanse of lake. As her father entered the room, she leapt into his arms and exclaimed, "I am so glad you are home. We need you around."

Her father held her, and Ahmeena unselfconsciously wept, as only a sixteen-year-old can. After many hugs and tears, the family sat in peaceful quiet and gazed at the fructiferous trees, as the sky that surrounded them went from orange to black. When Chester the cat had finally woke from his nap in the master bedroom and saw Khaled for the first time in over two years, he meowed loudly, jumped onto his master's lap, and began to paw and purr.

"Ah, Chester, I am glad to see you, and yes, I remember exactly how to pet you. Now, I hear you are the villain in this piece of business. We forgive you, Chester, but don't let it happen again. Now, Mary, tell me what has been going on with you. I am going fishing tomorrow with Jake, but I hope I do not have to wait that long to get my questions answered. I am worried when I look at you, all of this bruising, and your face. It looks so round and puffy; it is not the same face I have always known. It is still a most beautiful face, but it is different. Tell me: what is going on?"

"Khaled, there are two reasons why I look so bad, and I need to back up to what happened when I returned from our last Cairo vacation with you. I got off the plane and went directly into the hospital for three days. Dr. Hunter said he was worried I might get a clot from my heart not emptying fully between all the rapid irregular beats. So he started me on Coumadin to help thin my blood and prevent clotting. It also causes horrible bruising under any skin that is even slightly traumatized, as you can see. He has been regulating my Coumadin dose, according to twice-weekly blood tests, to make sure my blood doesn't get too thin. By the way, Ahmeena has been driving me to my appointments after school. She has been an angel, helping me, and excelling in school. We have much to be grateful for, Khaled.

"Anyway, Dr. Hunter warned me that my skin is becoming very fragile from taking the Prednisone all these years, and I was already on a higher dose when we were on vacation with you in Cairo. Do you know that Dr. Hunter said that if I ever had a flare up while away, I could increase my dose? Well, midway into our vacation, I increased my dose and felt great! I never had a chance to taper down the milligrams, because in the hospital with the atrial fib,

Dr. Hunter increased the dose even more. Every time I try to taper it down, I get a flare-up of increasing shortness of breath. I even have needed that portable oxygen machine. Do you see it behind the chair over there? Well, sometimes I have to sit down and put it on for a while, and when it is humid outside, I never go anywhere without it by my side. A side effect from the Prednisone is osteoporosis, and so, my bones may break more easily than they should. It is also causing my face to look like a full moon. To top it off, I now have purple stretch marks on my tummy. Dr. Hunter calls them striae, but I call them ugly! I am so happy you are home, but so sorry I am such a mess!"

Khaled gingerly squeezed Mary's shoulder and frowned. "Mary, I am upset that you have been through so much, and I wasn't around. Now I am home, and I will devote all my attention to you. I am home for good. I have gotten the Middle East out of my blood."

"Khaled, you have never told a lie in your life. Why do you start now? You will never get Majd Al Krum out of your system."

"This is true; its roots go deep within me. But, I have given up on mass communications. I will explore other avenues. I will work from home and be here for you. You are right; I misspoke. I will never get the Holy Land out of my blood. Oh, Mary, it has been devastating to me to learn of so much corruption in high places in the Arab nations. There is a terrible blindness and deafness to the suffering that surrounds the rich and the powerful. They do not see, nor hear the injustice that abounds. There is too much injustice in the world, and not enough voices demanding justice and showing the way to repair the mistakes of the past. But I have learned a lesson. I can only do the little good I see in front of me to do."

Khaled never slept that night, for he sat up in the chair next to the oxygen machine, watching Mary peacefully asleep on the sofa. At three o'clock in the morning, he brewed a pot of coffee, poured it into a large thermos, and soundlessly slipped out the French doors. He inhaled the essence of over-ripened fruit and was regaled by a symphony of crickets and frogs in heat. He tied the white handkerchief to his wrist and downed his fill of coffee, well before Jake coasted into the cattails and lily pads that filled the shoreline. The full moon dimly illuminated Khaled's path, and he almost slipped and fell into the sandy water three times before Jake suppressed a grin and held out his arm to help his friend.

Once Khaled had settled in safely, Jake slowly pressed the throttle to gain full speed, and did not stop until they reached the deepest part of the lake. Wordlessly, the men baited their hooks with foot-long live shiners, and silently cast off into deep, dark water. Not until Jake reeled in and released a seven pound bass did he light a cigar, pour a cup of coffee, and say, "Khaled, I am overwhelmed at your reticence and will not keep you in suspense any longer. Go ahead, unload, and ask your questions."

"My God, man. I feel so bad for all Mary has been through, and she never complains. Mary always thinks of others before herself; I will devote the rest of my life to thinking of her. Tell me the prognosis; I am ready for anything."

"Okay, Khaled, again, Mary's condition is progressing as expected. The sarcoidosis has invaded her heart muscle; there is only palliative treatment, and she is receiving all of that. The immediate future cannot be predicted, but you should be prepared, because if she falls again and breaks a hip, she may never recover. I can list a dozen scenarios that may or may not happen. Carpe diem, man; seize the day. Take every day with Mary as a gift. Nobody can predict the future, and I will not paint you a rosy picture. Everything we can do for Mary is being done. You love her and can spend time with her now, and you should."

"Thank you, my friend, can we go back now?"

"We have to. I have office appointments starting at nine and need to make hospital rounds."

CHAPTER 8:

THANKSGIVING EVE, 1987

JUST BEFORE SUNSET ON Wednesday, Bedouin drums began to sound across Lake Conway. Khaled was hosting a celebration and looking forward to making his announcements. Little Mo and Huda, his wife, had arrived the day before and were greeting guests at the front door.

On the porch, guests were greeted again by Mary and Ahmeena as they exited through the living room French doors. Mary sat in her wheelchair with her oxygen on. The first guest to reach her was Khadeejah, who had brought her cousin, Fatiha. She was a shy, soft-spoken Moroccan beauty, whom Mary warmly greeted. After catching up with Khadeejah, Mary turned to Fatiha and remarked, "My dear girl, what brought you to America?"

Fatiha cast her eyes down and whispered, "Mrs. Diab, I need a job."

"Mary, her family in Morocco has fallen on hard times, and Fatiha does not like to speak about her troubles. She only arrived in America last week, and has a one-year work visa. Perhaps someone here tonight will have a position for her."

Mary took pity on the young woman, patted her hand gently, and spoke. "Fatiha, stay next to me. You will meet everyone as they pass by on their way to the fire pit where the lamb is roasting. Perhaps your cousin is right. You may meet your future employer this very night. But for now, relax and enjoy the party."

After sunset prayers were said, and the guests had filled their plates, Khaled prepared himself to deliver his message. He stood at the edge of the orchard grove and lake that was illuminated with dozens of oil lamps, and gave thanks to God for so many friends and family. Over one hundred people sat on the sandy beach connecting the lake to the backyard grove.

When they all had noticed Khaled standing before them, they hushed their conversation, and he began. "My dear family and friends, we all have much to be grateful and thankful for this Thanksgiving eve. As you know, Mary and I have spent many a morning and evening right here where you all have gathered. Your presence here tonight now connects you to our future memories. I first want to give thanks to my daughter Ahmeena and her husband John for all their assistance tonight, and I thank all of you for the many side dishes and desserts you have contributed. Now, for my main news, I want to give thanks to God for being sixty-one years old and able to retire!

"I have decided that the time has come to close up shop at Technology International. I thank Mary for keeping the books all of these years and helping me in my endeavor, but the competition from Taiwan, Korea, and the Far East has caused me to surrender! I cannot compete with their cheap labor. I am grateful for the great success my invention of the Arabic telex received. Technology is changing rapidly, and I am ready to get out of its way and pursue new avenues of opportunity.

"Mary and I have had long discussions about the need for an Arab community center in Orlando. My vision is that we will establish a social and cultural venue for Arabs and Americans. It will be a haven, and a chance to keep our heritage alive and to celebrate the gifts of our people. So, here is to the demise of Technology International and the birth of a new vision: an Arab community center in Orlando. I welcome any and all help you wish to provide." The crowd erupted in clapping and laughing, and many promises of collaboration were made.

"Next, I have decided to rejoin the Middle East Communication Group, which many of you have still been attending. I agree to give it another chance, but if the dialogue becomes inflammatory and no positive action is taken, I will drop out again. I agree one needs to speak one's mind, but my focus is on where we should go from here. To continue playing the blame game will not get us anywhere. The time has come to move on to action, and my next step is to become a proactive participant in the cause of justice and peace! My plan and hope for the future is to care for Mary, establish an Arab American community center, and work for justice and peace!"

The crowd cheered, and everyone offered a prayer and blessing for Khaled and his family. Fatiha had never left Mary's side all evening and had met all the guests. When the revelers began to depart, Fatiha excused herself from Mary, immediately began cleaning up, and would not be dissuaded to stop. Not until everything had been cleaned up two hours later, did Fatiha agree to leave. Mary and Khaled then sat in happy silence, listening to the remaining friends and family who had gathered around the bonfire.

"Mary, you are glowing in the moonlight; you have radiance about you."

Mary smiled and softly spoke. "You must hire Fatiha as my nurse. The time has come for both of us to accept that I have become a burden. I need help getting in and out of this chair. I need help to brush my hair! I want some privacy back. I want a nurse! And I want Fatiha. Khaled, you have been the most wonderful, attentive, loving husband the world has ever known. But I am ready for and need to have a nurse. I want Fatiha! She is kind, soft, and gentle. She needs a job, and I need a nurse."

"But of course, Mary, I will call them in the morning. When I saw Fatiha happily cleaning up after such a crowd, I was thinking we should hire her as a housekeeper. I will call them in the morning, offer Fatiha a position as your nurse, and hopefully, she will continue to be happy to clean, too. But Mary, you must understand that I have been blessed to be of any little service to you. You have never been a burden. I have loved every moment with you. But, I agree, Fatiha will make a fine nurse and a fine companion. Now, Mary, let me tuck you in; the rest of our guests are very content around the bonfire, and I see you are very tired."

When Khaled returned to the bonfire, Little Mo was regaling the few remaining revelers with the details of his life. "Yes, yes, all my children are doing better than I had ever hoped or dreamed. Jamal and his family have been in Detroit since he graduated from Washington University in St. Louis with a Ph.D. in computer science. Nidal graduated from UCF, right here in Orlando, in electrical engineering. He is employed in Kuwait and planning his marriage. Diab is in Tallahassee, and that is where Huda and I are heading on Friday. It is our very first visit to their new home, and we will be staying with them for two weeks before we return to Kuwait. I am retiring next year as inspector of mathematics for all the Kuwait high schools, after a very long and eventful career. I have lived in Palestine, Damascus, and Amman, but Kuwait is home."

Just as Khaled emerged from the grove, Jake entered through the garden gate, holding both hands behind his back and chomping on a cigar. "Hello there. Sorry to miss the party, but Wednesday is half-day at the office, and I ran out to the woods. I knew there would be a nice fire going over here, so I thought I'd stop and say hello, and show you my bird."

And with that, he brought around a twenty-two pound tom turkey with all the feathers still on. "Just look at this fine specimen. Notice these inch-and-a-half-long pointy spurs of cartilage on his feet; watch out they don't stab you and draw blood. Notice his eleven-inch-long beard growing from his mid-chest like coarse strands of grey hair sprouting from an old crone's chin. Why, this is a geriatric bird; it probably would have died of old age in a few months and been devoured by buzzards. But, I have dispatched him for the Hunter family Thanksgiving."

Louise, the neighbor living around the corner, thought, What a hick! But she smiled and offered, "Jake, I have never known a physician like you. Every doctor I have ever known loves to golf, but you love to fish and play in the woods."

"Louise, it is my sanctuary. For me, the presence of God is manifest in nature. Some people connect to God in a manmade sanctuary, while my sanctuary is found in the earth, the sky, and any body of water around."

"Ah, a compatriot of the spirit! My name is Riad. Khaled has mentioned you to me many times."

"And you to me. I hope you all don't mind, but I'd like to pluck this tom by the light of your fire, and I am happy to share the essence of my stogie with you all." Jake smirked as he sat down.

The friends watched Jake rapidly denude the turkey as he shared his tale: "I sat motionless for hours in my turkey blind and never swatted even one mosquito. Hunting is about patience, stillness, and silence. It was over two hours before I heard the faint rustle of the flock of turkeys feeding not far from where I patiently sat. They took their time grazing towards me, and I counted six hens before I saw this old tom strut in. I knew I had found Thanksgiving dinner. I dispatched him painlessly with my shotgun and will be enjoying him smoked in a few hours. Now, Louise, I can tell you think I am heartless. Au contraire. You see, I believe having dominion over nature means to only harvest what one will consume. I do not hunt trophies. I hunt for food!"

Cid, who lived three homes down the street, commented, "Jake you are a piece of work, and thanks for sharing. But, Khaled, I want to pick back up where we left off. Even though I think the Middle East Communication Group is open to exploring solutions, there will always be a need for the group to vent their emotions. The daily news continues to keep us filled with new grief."

Louise nodded and said, "That's right. However, the turning point was when we all faced two blackboards, and one was labeled 'Jews' and the other 'Arabs' with STEREOTYPES printed in block letters on top. We all were shouting out every stereotype against the other we could think of. It went on and on; I was amazed that the lists kept growing, and so much pain was expressed. In fact, my husband was the one to stand up and walk over to the boards and write PAIN across each one.

"Everyone gasped and then the tears came. We all realized collectively that all our sharing was born out of deep pain. Many of us have arrived at the truth that if you are not part of the solution, you are part of the problem. Khaled, you are an idea man. You are able to imagine and envision solutions and implement plans to bring them into reality. We need your presence at the meetings and need to hear your voice. We are very pleased to hear you will be at the next meeting. Oh, here comes the loves of my life, Frank and Sammie. It's time for me to go."

Frank and the schnauzer greeted the group, and Cid stood and announced, "I'll walk with you."

Louise stretched, locked eyes with Khaled, and said, "What we need are more people who are impatient with evil and patient with people--more people with the courage to fight for social justice and not worry that when they step out on nothing but the truth, it will be a very long time before they get to land, but when they do, it will be on very sound ground."

Jake finished plucking his bird, sat back, and declared, "Before you go, I have a few questions about your Middle East Communications Group. I want to know why there are never any moderate Muslims speaking out against the terrorists. Why, when Sadat was assassinated back in 1981 by radical Muslims, did none of the Muslims condemn the murder, and still haven't? Sadat was making progress. Peace seemed possible over there, and his own people murdered him."

Cid agreed readily. "Jake, that is a problem the Jewish people also express. Moderate Muslims are too often mute, but I never hesitate to condemn terrorism when it comes from our leaders in Israel or America."

Khaled jumped up and began to pace around the fire, and the neighbors sat back down. "Yes, I agree that any terrorism is wrong, and the misguided Muslims who do such things are not following what the Koran really teaches. What the Koran proclaims is the unity, omnipotence, omniscience, and mercy of God, as well as the total dependence of human life upon him.

"The Koran has 192 references to God's compassion and mercy, and only 17 references to his wrath and vengeance. The true meaning of infidel is one who is ungrateful, or one who denies the existence of the Supreme Being. Everyone gathered here tonight is a person of the book and should never be labeled infidels. I am sorry for the actions of those who are focused on wrath and vengeance, violence and destruction. They are not like any Muslims I know! I do understand they are acting out of a deep despair caused by the injustice they have been acutely living with for fifty years. Until we address the root of the problem, there will be continued instability in the Middle East.

"Each violent retaliation only solidifies the opponent's despair, and more violence is their answer. First Sadat was assassinated, and then twenty thousand Muslims were killed in a twenty-seven day bombing in the city of Hama, for that had been their headquarters among the innocent. This overkill of innocent people must stop. Tell me, Jake, how do you justify the 1982 Israeli-backed Christian militia, which annihilated 1,000-1,500 Palestinian and Lebanese civilians in Sabra and Shatilla refugee camps? Ariel Sharon was in charge of the training, and he trained the attackers in the art of terrorism! Why isn't he being condemned for terrorism, too?"

Cid jumped in. "Khaled, I agree; that attack was unjustified murder, and Sharon and the entire Israeli government should be held accountable."

Jake spoke while chewing on his cigar. "Hey, that's a good point; I don't even remember hearing about any investigation into that matter. But I am more concerned about all the plane hijackings and learning about the Israeli nuclear program. Last October, when I took Terese to London for our anniversary, I read an incredible story of a Jew named Mordechai Vanunu in the London Sunday Times.[18] He had worked in a very compartmentalized position for years, in the secret underground Dimona nuclear research center in the Negev. When he finally realized he was involved in horrific work, he shot extensive photos inside the factory to document what was going on. He left Israel and carried around the undeveloped film for a year throughout Europe and ended up in Sydney, where he converted to Christianity and shared his story with a British reporter. Vanunu and the reporter returned to London, and while the paper was verifying the photos, Vanunu mysteriously disappeared. The photos prove the fact that Israel had become a major nuclear power. Last year, Israel's underground plutonium plant had material for two hundred nuclear warheads of advanced design, and I have never heard a word about it from the US media. It makes me wonder about the iron curtains the media or politicians can raise as a shield."

Riad spoke. "That's not all, Jake, and the facts are that even before that story ran, the Mossad had lured Mordechai to Italy, abducted him, and dumped his drugged body onto an Israeli cargo vessel bound for Israel. Vanunu has been charged with treason and is being tried in a closed-door trial."

Khaled stretched his legs toward the fire and looked at Cid as he spoke. "Jake, Israeli's nuclear program has been an open secret for some time, but has never received attention from the American press. I know my Palestinian brethren have done many bad things. I do not excuse or defend them. But, when they see America turn a blind eye to the many bad things the Israelis do, well, it just continues the cycle."

Jake chewed his cigar as he spoke. "If I may play devil's advocate here, I would say Israel is only trying to protect itself from hostile neighbors. But then, by that logic, why shouldn't the twenty-two Arab countries also have the right to do the same? All I know is that the first casualty of war is Mother Nature. The killing of innocent people and destruction of the environment has become acceptable collateral damage. God is within all life, and creation is God's dwelling place. Besides, people are to be caretakers of creation. No religion owns God, and no people can own any land. The best they can do is possess. I hate to think what the Supreme Being feels when we obliterate the face and word of God in creation. Be it with bombs or over construction, it makes me crazy when people are blind to the sacredness of all life. Jesus taught me to pray for my enemies, forgive my enemies, and do good towards my enemies. It's no wonder they crucified him. That message was not popular then, nor is it now."

Khaled stared into the fire as he spoke. "Too many people choose the way of violence and oppression to ensure a sense of safety. Violence breeds retaliation, despair, and hopelessness. Violence will never beget peace. Guns and bombs don't solve anything; they cause nothing but pain. The earth suffers from the destruction of life, be it human, animal, or plant. Jake, you have given me some more food for thought on this Thanksgiving Day."

"I am happy to serve. Speaking of which, in just a few hours, I will be thankfully serving this bird to my family. It's time to wake Terese so she can start smoking it! My sister Brigid from Ireland would insist I invite you all over, too. She arrived six days ago and hasn't stopped cooking since. Happy Thanksgiving to you all, and now I will take my turkey and go home."

After the neighbors left for their homes, Riad, Little Mo, and Khaled were alone. They watched the dying embers of the fire until Little Mo said, "Let us share our last prayer together now before retiring. It has been a long, eventful day, and we all need to rest and reflect."

Riad added, "I agree. Our friend Jake reminds me of the nineteenth-century Scottish mystic, Alexander Scott, who also understood that "creation is a transparency through which a light of God is seen."[19]

CHAPTER 9:

THE END BRINGS YOU BACK AROUND

MARY SPENT THREE DAYS on a respirator in intensive care at Florida Hospital on Lake Rowena, after suffering a seizure while sitting at her olivewood table. Khaled camped out in the ICU waiting room, and each morning at daybreak, he was riveted at the picture window hours before the sky transformed from obscure to radiant.

For hours, he watched the Spanish moss undulate in the expansive oak trees that dotted the shore. At seven o'clock in the morning, the team of physicians began making rounds, and he thoroughly questioned every one of them after they examined Mary. At nine, he was allowed to sit at Mary's bedside for fifteen minutes and hold her hand in the midst of tubing and wires. When the nurses kindly told him his time was up, he reluctantly returned to the waiting room until he was allowed to go back. He knew that when the anhingas and cormorants began their sunbathing in the noonday sun, it would not be too much longer. For three days, he was grateful for three twelve-minute daily visits with Mary.

Ahmeena dropped Fatiha off in the morning to stay with him and returned after school to take Fatiha home. But Khaled would not leave the hospital. By the evening of the fourth day, Mary had been weaned successfully from the respirator, but had not regained consciousness. She was being transferred to a private room in the progressive care unit where the trio waited.

Just as Mary was being wheeled down the hall, Khaled gave in to Ahmeena. "Yes, I agree. Fatiha will be with your mother all day tomorrow. I promise, I will go home then and sleep until tomorrow evening. Then I will spend tomorrow night with Mary, and Fatiha can go home and rest. But tonight, I want to sit beside Mary and speak from my heart. I trust she can hear me. As Jake said, the hearing is the last to go."

After the nurses reattached Mary to a heart monitor and readjusted her oxygen cannula, the family gathered around her bed and offered a prayer. Ahmeena hugged her father and said, "Dad, I really need to go. John and the kids need me at home. Tomorrow, after I drop the kids at school, I will bring Fatiha back here and take you home!"

"I promise I will go quietly, but now you two, go home, and leave my wife and me alone." He smiled for the first time since Mary had read him the Garfield comic strip four days prior. Immediately afterward, she suffered the violent convulsion that left her in a coma. Khaled waved the women out the door, and then closed it gently. He sat in a chair that he had pulled up beside Mary's ear, held her hand, and softly spoke.

"Ah, Mary, I finally have time to share the mail with you. The other day we received a letter from Jack Hunt on the occasion of his twentieth year, clean and sober. It's the seven-year anniversary of him founding The BLAC: Brother Lawrence Addiction Center. He sent this poem that he wrote and hung on his office wall. I'll read it to you.

"'Peace, peace, peace. God's peace be upon you. But living today in a time of war, crying out peace, peace, peace, when there is no peace. Fearing age and death, pain and darkness, destitution and loneliness, people need to get back to the simplicity of Brother Lawrence.' -Dorothy Day.[20]

"'Brother Lawrence was a monk in the seventeenth century, who lived in a monastery and was consigned to the kitchen. He spent his life baking bread, chopping onions, scrubbing pots and floors. He ran all the errands, did all the shopping, and always brought back the finest wine. He loved his brothers deeply, but they merely tolerated his many eccentricities, or he was totally ignored. Truly, I tell you, if ever a saint was born to bring hope to the addicted and those afflicted with obsessive-compulsive tendencies, he is the one. For Brother L. learned that by continually re-remembering the Lord, no matter what the activity, or where one might be, the Lord was ever present and a holy habit was born, just remembering that.'"

Khaled folded the letter with fingers quivering as much as his lower lip. A tear fell on Mary's mouth, and he imagined that she said thank you.

"Jack certainly made peace with that tragic accident in the car I gave him when we moved. I have felt guilty for years, believing that if I had not given him the keys, the accident never would have happened, he would have been able to continue receiving his football scholarship, and maybe he wouldn't have suffered with so many addictions. He sends you his love and also this photo of him and his beautiful new bride, Julianne.

"Mary, that reminds me of our daughter's beautiful wedding and how happy you were. How many nights did you work until dawn, sewing all those bridesmaids' dresses! And now, we have little Mary and little Jake. Oh, Mary, my heart breaks to imagine what our lives would be like if I had never been able to make a new life in America. There would be no Ahmeena and no grandchildren. You would have married another, and I might have been a bachelor!"

As Khaled sat back and chuckled, he thought he saw Mary move her lips. As he leaned in closely, he heard her murmur, "Khaled, marry Fatiha."

Stunned, Khaled bolted backwards and began to tremble. "Mary, my love, we have been one for forty-three years; you don't know what you are saying." Mary never again regained consciousness. Nine hours later, as silently as a butterfly hovers above a flower, she entered into eternity.

Six months later, Khaled shuffled through the newly built Orlando International Airport to start the first leg of his journey back to Majd Al Krum. He had insisted on taking this trip alone. As he walked, he thought, I cannot believe how much growth Orlando has seen in these twenty-odd years. It is phenomenal. America has so many opportunities for people who will work hard; they can all realize a future with hope.

Abruptly, he muttered aloud, "Damn you, Mary!" He looked sheepishly around and was grateful nobody paid him any attention. He thought, Mary, I cannot yet bear the thought of never holding you again; is too painful to bear. I respect and admire Fatiha. She has been a wonderful nurse and companion to you, a friend to me, and like a big sister to our daughter. Fatiha is already a part of our family! In fact, Ahmeena wanted her to accompany me on my next journey, but I want to take this trip alone, with you in my mind. I do not want to think any further into the future right now. I will think of that when I return to Orlando.

He thought of his brother Hamid, who would be picking him up at the Ben Guerin Airport after his first stop. Generations of Diabs continued to live in the same house that Khaled had left fifty years before. Hamid had told him of the many changes in Majd Al Krum since he had fled. The population was fourteen hundred when he had lived there, and now it was over twelve thousand and still growing. Many olive groves had been uprooted for housing. When Khaled was a boy, the closest school was hours away in the town of Acre. Now, over two thousand children receive an education in their own neighborhood, and many go on to become professionals. Khaled smiled at the thought that one thing remained constant: families stayed together.

Khaled imagined Mary at his side and silently spoke to her. "I may have moved far away and traveled the world over, but my heart has never left Majd Al-Krum. But, after I land in Lebanon, I am going to spend my first night in the Shatilla refugee camp. From there, I will fly to Cyprus and on to Tel Aviv, where Hamid will pick me up and drive me home to Majd Al Krum."

Hours after all the passengers had been asleep, Khaled recalled the day he and Mary had driven in the center lane of the broad bridge that led into Canada. "The border patrolmen approached, and I rolled down my window and naïvely said, 'Hello?'

"'Hello to you, and where were you born?' that officer inquired, and I began to tremble.

"'In Palestine,' I proudly said._

"Then he turned to you and said, 'And you, ma'am?'

"'Fort Dodge, Iowa.'

"'Then he turned back to me and shook his head as he said, 'Alright, sir, exit the car, please. May I see your papers? Good, now follow me. Ma'am, please wait here.' I felt every eye from every car bore through me, as I followed behind the two lanes of stopped vehicles and entered into the office, where my green card, passport, and identification were carefully examined. Then, I was told with a smile, 'Okay, you are free to go!'

"How difficult it was for me to walk back peacefully to you before I exploded, 'Just because I was born in Palestine, I am considered a threat. I cannot bear to think how my Palestinian brethren must feel when they are confronted daily with demands to show proof of who they are! It is so unjust! First, the secular Zionists scared us out of our homes. They forced us to be refugees! And the Arab leadership is failing the people! There is no justice in the Holy Land. Palestinians are being born and dying in refugee camps, when for centuries, we lived on the land where our forefathers tended and cultivated fruitful trees of citrus and olive.'

"Oh, sure, the UN passed Resolution 194 to allow my people to return home or be compensated, and it has yet to be enforced! No Palestinian can travel freely; they are all stopped and interrogated. It happened to me just that once, but I am still livid just the same! Being discriminated against because of where one was born--it's unjust! Injustice only breeds despair that births death. In my brain, I constantly hear Riad speaking, and Jake informed me that Pope Paul VI also says it all the time, too: 'If you want peace, you must fight for justice.' Their words torment me. I want peace, but I do not know how to fight the fight for justice. I keep seeing parallels to what the American Indian and the American Negro have suffered because of injustice. My heart breaks, for my Palestinian brethren have no one fighting to bring justice to them. They have been forgotten by the world. I have not forgotten them; how I wish I knew what to do to help them."

It was hours more before Khaled finally gave in to slumber. He dreamt he was in a long corridor with many closed doors. He walked slowly for what seemed like hours, until he spied two huge cathedral-size doors at the end of the long corridor. As he approached, they opened into the hidden space beyond and invitingly beckoned him in. He stood upon a mountaintop, and for miles and miles, he did see a Holy Land, wholly covered in olive trees. And everywhere were people of the human family, diverse in color, and of every creed. And they all rested in peace and harmony beneath the shade of olive trees.

When he woke up, he thought he heard Riad whisper in his ear:
'You must give birth to your images.
They are the future waiting to be born.
Fear not the strangeness you feel.
The future must enter you long before it happens.'[21]

When Khaled disembarked in Lebanon, he hailed a cab and requested to be driven directly to the Shatilla refugee camp. The driver looked at him quizzically, but Khaled never noticed. His thoughts were of Mary, until the driver announced, "Here you are."

As Khaled looked through the windshield, he was overwhelmed with a sense of desolation and foreboding. "My God, here I have been feeling sorry for myself for losing the love of my life, and have enjoyed such comfort and security. Shatilla looks like a prison. I cannot imagine what I would be like today if I had remained at Shatilla. It looks like a suburban housing project for the indigent, with so many people crammed into such a small place. I was determined to spend the night, but now I see there may be no room for me, or anyone else at this inn!"

As Khaled neared the entrance, an old Palestinian with a deeply creviced and weather-worn face squinted at Khaled and snarled, "You look like an American; what are you doing here?"

"I am Khaled Diab, a Palestinian-American."

"Khaled Diab, from Majd Al-Krum? It is you? I am Abu Hassan, your cousin. Don't you recognize me? Remember when you and I walked together for twenty-one hours from home to Lebanon? It is so good to see you. I never had the chance to thank you for rescuing my son from here so he could go to school in America! And because he had that opportunity, he rescued his two brothers, and they have all graduated with degrees!"

After a lot of hugging and tears of joy at their reunion, Abu Hassan led Khaled by the hand through the twisting narrow alleys that snaked haphazardly through the over-crowded housing. "You must stay with my family tonight. Umm Hassan and I had one child when we entered here five decades ago. Now, we are a family of thirty-one, counting all the grandchildren."

Khaled was distraught to see naked toddlers playing in mud mixed with sewage and crying for something to eat. He saw young boys playing ball in the alleys between the tenements. He walked by a school and heard children singing praises of their homeland, and he gave thanks for something positive, although he mourned the fact that they would probably never see it. When they reached the particular door that looked like hundreds of others along the narrow street, Abu Hassan turned and commanded, "Wait here."

When Abu Hassan reopened the door, five young men bolted out, and Khaled was welcomed in. Flat bread and *zatar* were placed on the table, and he was warmly invited to sit. Word traveled rapidly, and within minutes, neighbors began appearing, bringing pots and dishes of food to share. All Khaled could say was "Thank you for your hospitality, but I have come to visit with the hope of helping you."

Abu Hassan lifted his arms and exclaimed, "But you already have when you sponsored Hassan. Now we have three college graduates in the family, and they send us money for food and clothing. If we were able to migrate anywhere, our boys would provide for us. Oh, Khaled, if only you could tell the world not to ignore us. We really only want justice! We are not idiots. We know our homes and olive groves have been plowed down. Resolution 194 stated that those who were forced from the land in 1948 should be allowed to return or be compensated. I am still waiting! I still have the key to my door. See? I wear it on a chain around my neck and wonder if it will still fit my front door. I am not an idiot; I know I have no home left, now. I would be grateful just to get out of this camp and put down new roots somewhere. We cannot get passports. We cannot come and go as free citizens. We are prisoners, and all because we were born Palestinian."

Khaled prayed for words, but none came. Abu Hassan continued. "Did you notice the young men who left when you arrived? They are *Fedayeen* freedom fighters. They grew up witnessing explosions that left men, women, children, and everything around them turned into charcoal. They grew up with helicopters, fighter planes, and tanks shooting at them. Even with the disparity in weapons, they believe they will liberate their people and themselves. They have been fed a diet of discrimination because they are refugees, people without a country. They have been taught to love their homeland, although they have never seen it. And now, the West calls the only ones who help us terrorists, while we know them as service providers! These militant groups have reached out to the young in our camp and have built schools and hospitals, and are very well organized. They provide services to the entire community, whether you join them or not; they do not discriminate."

An ancient, yet strikingly tall, thin man with wide shoulders and penetrating eyes that appeared translucent at the same time had been leaning against the wall, listening and watching. When he cleared his throat, everyone hushed and turned towards him, and he spoke directly to Khaled. "Sir, do you remember me? I remember you; we both walked in the dark that October night so long ago. I was the one who shook the carob tree so you, your family, and others could quench their thirsts. It is true that despite the evil they perpetrate, the Lebanese Hezbollah have provided us with a lot of comfort and support in the camp. I follow the Christian path, and I would like to know why the Christians in the West don't do something to help us receive justice. Are the teachings of Jesus nothing to them but empty slogans?"[22]

Khaled could only shrug and pray for an answer, as a flute began playing a familiar tune that changed the mood into a festive celebration. New neighbors kept arriving until after midnight, but the shepherd was ignored. When sleep began to overtake the crowd, Abu Hassan motioned Khaled to follow him outside, and the shepherd followed along. The trio stood under a full moon, and Khaled said, "Abu Hassan, I made a substantial living in the United States in the defense industry. Now, I wonder about a new kind of defense. Imagine if there were a branch in the American military that trained soldiers to provide community service; imagine the changes we might see in the world. Ah, it is only a dream, I know. Abu Hassan, I will take my leave when the sun begins to rise, and I thank you for your hospitality. I must continue on my journey back to Majd Al-Krum. My dear wife has passed away, and I am planting an olive tree there in her honor."

Abu Hassan looked deep into Khaled's eyes and boldly asked, "Will you plant one for my family, too?"

"Of course I will plant one for you. And then I will plant another one. Why, in fact, that's a great idea, Abu Hassan. Maybe I will plant a million trees! Say, can you imagine if a million olive trees were planted amass in the Holy Land? Why, imagine millions of trees being replanted where they had once grown, but have now been plowed down.

"Why, imagine the jobs that would generate. The local plant nurseries would have to hire, and the people who would plant the trees and tend them would receive more than trees. They would receive a gift of hope and a gift of peace. Imagine the harvesting of millions of olive trees and all the oil that would be pressed! Imagine industry to package soaps and jars of olives! Imagine the exportation of Holy Land olive oil! Imagine the youth of the Holy Land having a future with hope. Imagine Americans providing the funds for those olive trees! Why, the world would again see we are a people of compassion and generosity, a people who desire peace. Imagine the people of the Holy Land and America working together, planting olive trees like sisters and brothers! Why, I imagine peace, reconciliation and opportunity. Yes! That's it! Go PRO: possibilities for peace, reconciliation, and opportunity for all."

The shepherd cleared his throat and promised, "Blessed are the peacemakers; they shall be called the children of God."[23]

CHAPTER 10:

THAT DAY

KHALED, NOW SEVENTY-FIVE AND a newlywed since July, turned to Fatiha and cried, "This madness must stop. Retaliation only ups the ante, and the wheel is still in spin. But I am nearing my end. I have been dreaming of mass communication for decades and olive trees my entire life; now, I must act!"

Within hours of viewing the news, he had phoned many friends: Jews, Christians, Muslims, and others to gather in downtown Orlando at Lake Eola and pray for peace. He told everyone, "Praying for peace without action is like praying to win the lottery and never buying a ticket. But unless we work for peace, saying 'peace, peace, peace,' means nothing. If we want peace, we must work for justice."

Jack had been restless for three days. Julianne was in New York City at her sister's home and wasn't due back for three more. His knees began throbbing more the moment she drove out of sight on the morning of September 8, 2001.

After returning home on Monday night from the BLAC, Brother Lawrence Addictions Center, Jack mindlessly ate two Lean Cuisines, then spent the rest of the evening trying to read. He fell asleep just before dawn and dreamt he was on the blacktop running track at the middle school where Julianne taught seventh grade English, where they both rollerbladed in the early mornings before the kids came to campus.

Jack spent a ten-hour day at the BLAC, as its founder and administrator, and the mornings on the track were when the couple had their best conversations. He inhaled the aroma of tar as he wondered what was keeping Julianne from him. He bladed for what seemed like hours, when a silver spandex-clad apparition with a golden helmet flew by, sharply turned, and with a backward stroke, called out, "Hi, Jack, don't look down; don't look back; look out straight, Jack, look out straight, don't look back!"

"Yeah, I can; I can do that," Jack bellowed, but the apparition had already vaporized into the distance. Then Jack rolled onto an exquisite grace, knees freed from bone-on-bone grinding and not an ache in his fifty-three-year-old body that had been abused by two motor vehicle accidents and hours of overuse syndrome. Jack glided on the blacktop effortlessly for what seemed like hours, when suddenly, a roar of thunder assaulted his senses, and his eyes were magnetized upward, to view two fireballs thrown down from on high, miles from where he stood. He saw them hit the ground; one traveled east, the other west, and then they circled back around, burning a path straight towards him. Just before they collided, Jack woke up, not believing he had only been dreaming.

Not until after he had downed a pot of coffee did the phone ring. "Jack? Are you watching TV?" Maureen, the day supervisor at the BLAC asked, as she fingered the framed mission statement that sat upon every desk and on the north wall of every room:

> 'Peace, peace, peace. God's peace be upon you. But living today in a time of war, crying out peace, peace, peace, where there is no peace. Fearing age and death, pain and darkness, destitution and loneliness, people need to get back to the simplicity of Brother Lawrence.' [Dorothy Day]
>
> Brother L. was a monk in the 17th century, who lived in a monastery and was consigned to the kitchen. He spent his life baking bread, chopping onions, scrubbing pots and floors. He ran all the errands, did all the shopping, and always brought back the finest of wine. He loved his brothers deeply, but they merely tolerated his many eccentricities, or he was totally ignored. Truly, I tell you, if ever a saint was born to bring hope to the addicted and those afflicted with obsessive-compulsive tendencies, he is the one. For Brother L. learned that by continually re-remembering the Lord, no matter what the activity, or where one might be, the Lord was ever-present and a holy habit was born, just re-remembering that.

Jack thrived on curiosity and spoke as he reached for the remote. "Mo, you know I never watch TV in the daytime; what's up?"

"Well, isn't Julianne visiting her sister in the city?"

"Yeah, in fact, today's plan was to meet her sister's co-workers on Floor 101 of the North Twin Tower."

"Jack, turn the TV on."

"Oh, Mo, I just did; my God, is it the end of the world?" He spoke as he hung up the phone and never heard Mo say, "I don't know."

Jack knew in his bones that Julianne had been vaporized as he recalled a song he had first heard in 1981:

See the massacre of the innocent

City's on fire

Phones out of order

I see the turning of the page.

Curtain's rising on a new age.

See the Groom still waiting at the altar.[Bob Dylan, Shot of Love, Columbia Records, Inc. 1981]

And then, II Chronicles 6:1 welled up within him: "The Lord has said that he would dwell in thick darkness."

Dr. Jake Hunter heard the news that stopped the world for a day from his third patient of the morning. Terese didn't know until Jake called her before his next patient.

Kat had been dancing in her loft studio in Panacea, Florida, all morning, ignoring neurological symptoms. She did not turn her cell phone on until 11:45 a.m., and then gasped, "Christ, who died? The entire Hunter clan has called me. I'll phone Mom," she said, just as "Let it Be" chimed from her cell.

"Hi, Kat, I have been trying to reach you."

"Mom, what's the deal? What's going on?"

"Turn the TV on."

Kat did and gasped, "Oh my God, is it the end of the world?"

"Nobody knows."

"Mom, I am coming home. I'll bring Bob; I think I'll stay awhile."

"Okay, okay, drive carefully."

Kat packed three weeks' worth of clothes, put Bob, her blue-eyed cat, in his kennel, and wrote a sign for the front door that read "KATZ STUDIO CLOSED UNTIL???"

She taped it to the door and never looked back again. "Bob, I have been dreading telling dad about my symptoms, because I don't want to admit them. But, I have been summoned from the land of denial and must face the facts on the ground. If I have the dreaded Gehrig's disease like my cousin Nick, I will be livid. He was a saint; I am not. I am not dancing as I once did; I don't glide anymore, I have gotten clumsy, and all of these muscle twitches are driving me crazy! I am pissed! I am too young for this! Oh Christ, I hope it is just a bad cervical spine, like Dad's. I can live with the pain, but I must be able to move about, or I'll go nuts. Nick was a saint even when he couldn't move, but I will be an unholy terror if I can't dance. Bob, if I have ALS, will you please just shoot me and put everyone out of my misery?"

Kat sighed deeply and popped in a favorite mix she had burned of Tom Petty and U2, and then lost herself until Bono began to wail:

If I could yes I would,
If I could, I would let it go
Into the half light and through the flame
Into the light and to the day,
Let it go and so to find the way,
To let it go, and so to find the way.
I am wide awake, I am wide awake, wide awake
If I could, you know I would:
Let it go:
Desperation,
Dislocation,
Separation,
Condemnation,
Revelation,
In temptation,
Isolation,
Desolation,
Let it go and so to find a way
I am wide awake,
I am wide awake,
I am wide awake, wide awake!

Kat mused, "Strange, how seeing that horror on TV woke me up to some things, too."

The Sunday after that day the world stood still, the Hunters' seven children and eighteen grandchildren had gathered together. Everyone was down at the lake except for Jake, Terese, and Kat, who were in the family room.

Jake contemplated Kat's chances of having ALS or a bad neck, and brooded.

Terese said, "There's an interfaith gathering today in Shea Stadium, and I want to view it."

She turned the TV on just as the *shofar* sounded in New York City, and hundreds of priests, rabbis, sheiks, and clerics of all kinds filed into the stadium in front of a sorrowful nation. Kat became luminous. "Wow, look at how beautiful all of that is! All of those holy ones in their uniqueness and all the shades of people in the stands reaching out to each other--how blessed we are in America to live among such diversity, and how beautiful it is to see us coming together out of such sorrow. This is the way we can let the pain go: by reaching out to the stranger, we comfort them and heal ourselves. America's worst day has brought us and the world together. Why, it's only a few angry mad men who did the evil; the international community can confront this together, by confronting this evil as sister and brother. What an incredible opportunity America has been given to lead the world this way and not seek revenge. Imagine the dysfunctional family of Father Abraham building on this momentum, to confront the evil that is terrorism, by confronting it with good and unity among us. Didn't St. Paul say that the only way to resist evil is with good? Imagine how much better the world will be when America chooses not to use military power, now that we all know our nuclear arsenal cannot protect us American's will want to discover why these mad men did this evil and go after that! The global village is the community to address this issue; terrorism is everywhere, and now America has woken up to the fact that we are not immune. We are all in this world together; we will either learn to share this world as sister and brother, or we will blow it up."

Terese responded. "Kat, human nature is to strike back and seek revenge, but we have witnessed from Christ, Gandhi, and Reverend King how to effectively respond to violence. I hope and pray this president follows their ways, but I see hawks circling."

Jake cleared his throat and intoned, "Another thing is that acting out of fear makes one do stupid, irrational things. You know I have always said to never ever react out of fear, for the gospel says fear not! And fear drives out compassion and hardens the heart."

Kat was mesmerized by the TV, Terese sighed deeply repeatedly, and Jake brooded.

In a log cabin nestled within the thickly wooded mountains of upstate New York, Jack sat in a darkened room with the TV on, but he wasn't watching. When the *shofar* blew and grabbed his attention, he froze until the ram's horn went silent, and then popped open his sixth beer of the day, for Jack had fallen off the wagon.

CHAPTER 11:

16 DAYS IN ISRAEL PALESTINE

The Peace of the World begins in Jerusalem

--Rev. Theodore Hessburgh

TEN INTERFAITH FRIENDS FROM the U.S. branch of the Olive Trees Foundation for Peace arrived in Tel Aviv on Sunday morning, June 12, 2005, at 3 a.m. Everyone else settled in their beds at the Ambassador Hotel in East Jerusalem, but Jack was wide awake. After a shower, he wandered through the East Jerusalem streets in the dark, and reached the Western Wall just as the sun rose. He walked the empty Via Delarosa and wondered, "Where are all the Christians? I have seen videos of this place with packed streets, and this morning, I am totally alone."

Jack wandered into the courtyard at the Anglican St. George's Cathedral just before noon. He was staring at a statue of St. Francis in a winding, flower-filled courtyard, and thought, "Hmmm--Frankie--you remind me of Julianne. She always greeted everyone with 'As Francis of Assisi said to Brother Dominic when their paths crossed on the road to Umbria: HI!'" Jack lost himself in good memories before that Tuesday in September when everything changed. He shivered when he heard the snap of gum sound as loudly as Julianne's ever had. He turned and saw a compact balding man of about fifty move by swiftly and enter the guest house. The man rang the bells everyday at noon, and had just descended the bell tower. Jack thought, I think that's Vanunu. I had no clue he was so short.

When Julianne lost her life in a stairway of the Twin Towers that day in September, Jack fell off the wagon. While in rehab for the last time, he also began watching a lot of TV. He caught a show on the History Channel entitled "Sexpionage." It was all about Russian female spies and one from the *Mossad*. Jack had a faint memory of hearing briefly about Mordechai Vanunu in 1986, but everything else he saw that night was news to him. He learned that Vanunu had a low-tech position in the underground Dimona nuclear plant in the Negev. When Vanunu had a crisis of conscience about being a cog in the making of weapons of mass destruction, he copped the keys to the restricted areas and shot two rolls of film that proved Israel had gone nuclear. He resigned and left the country, but did not develop the film until nearly a year later. Vanunu had ended up in Sydney, where he was baptized a Christian and met Peter Hounam, a journalist for the *Sunday Times*. Peter flew Vanunu to London and began to check out the story, which took more days than Vanunu had patience to bear in solitude. Out of boredom, Vanunu ventured out and met an American named Cindy. He had no clue she worked for the *Mossad*. After a week of movies and museums, he traveled with her to Rome, where her sister had an apartment. When Vanunu entered the apartment, he was hit on the head, drugged, bound, and flung upon an Israeli cargo ship heading home. The *London Times* broke the story just as Vanunu disappeared. The world did not know if Vanunu was alive or dead. They found out while he was being transported to his closed-door trial. Vanunu had been inspired to write "HIJACKED" on his palm, with the Rome flight number he had been on. This really agitated the Israeli government, and from then on, Vanunu was shielded from the world. He was sentenced to eighteen years for treason and was released in April of 2004, but remains under house arrest and has been living in St. George's guest house ever since.

The show also ran video from 1986 of Shimon Perez telling the world that Israel would never be the first country in the Middle East to go nuclear. Jack thought for a long time about whether he should approach Vanunu, who had set up his laptop underneath an umbrella table a few feet away. Jack never missed an opportunity.

"Pardon me; you are Vanunu, aren't you?"

Vanunu nodded and shook Jack's hand, while Jack remained standing; Vanunu returned to his laptop. "I want you to know how much I admire you, for your courage and for speaking the truth. I am leaving for the Galilee tomorrow, but if our paths cross when I return to Jerusalem; I would like to invite you to dinner."

Vanunu nodded; Jack left and didn't think anymore about it.

When he arrived at the Ambassador, he saw Khaled Diab, Founder of the Olive Trees Foundation for Peace, in the lobby at a table meeting with a slightly built, incessantly chain-smoking man. As Jack approached, Khaled rose from his chair and greeted him like a well-loved son. Then he turned to his companion and told Jack, "This is Hasan Suwan. He is the coordinator for PARC, the Palestinian Agricultural Relief Committee. As you know, PARC has been doing all the assessing for the need for trees, and assuring the planting and upkeep is being done. He will travel with us to last season's planting sites and help us discover next season's. He was just telling me the problems the wall has caused him, because he is an Israeli citizen married to a Palestinian."

Jack unabashedly asked, "Mr. Suwan, will you tell me more? I have come to Israel and Palestine in support of my good friend and second father, Khaled. I have sought the truth my entire life; please tell me everything about what life is like for you and yours in Israel and Palestine."

"Well, my wife has Palestinian papers, which means she cannot come with me into Israeli territory. Every six months, she must fill out papers and wait in line all day before she is told yes or no. The papers are her permission to leave Palestinian territory. I have Israeli ID, and I cannot go into Palestinian territories, because, I am told, the IDF could not ensure my safety if I went to visit my family! If an Israeli citizen takes a Palestinian in his car and is caught, he is fined five thousand shekels, and the car is confiscated for a month. Before the wall, my wife was able to walk to her mother's home in less than fifteen minutes. Now, it takes an hour and a half to drive through the checkpoints, and one can be told, 'No, you cannot enter. Go back from where you came.' Then, one either does go back, or looks for another way around. In my town of Jabal Al Mukaber, the concrete fence divides our family. So far, the wall has uprooted over two million trees." Hasan lit another cigarette and smirked as he told Jack, "For Palestinians, the worst tragedies make us laugh."

That morning, Jack had been reading "A Call for Morally Responsible Investment: A Nonviolent Response to the Occupation." [Sabeel Document No. 3, 2005: www.sabeel.org] As Suwan was speaking, Jack kept imagining thousands of Caterpillar tractors plowing up ancient olive groves, and wondered if his church was investing in that company. He wondered if the Olive Trees Foundation for Peace could ever keep pace with the demand for trees as the wall tore down even more.

On Monday night, the ten met over thirty of Khaled's family in a restaurant and became fast friends. Jack, a serious Christian of the Beatitudes and struggling Episcopalian, broke bread with Muslims, who all agreed that all everyone really wanted was for their children to be able to live in peace. They all were educating their children in mixed schools, and struggled with the daily worry of children crossing checkpoints.

Khaled's nephew, a fertility specialist, told Jack, "My wife and I try very hard to keep the reality of life from affecting our children. We teach them that we all must be peaceful to all others. But, they ask many questions that I cannot answer, such as, 'Is President Bush a friend to Palestinians?'"

Jack bit his lip and went silent for the rest of the night.

Tuesday, June 14, 2005: The Upper Galilee and a secular Jewish prophet

While riding in the van with their ten friends, Jake and Terese Hunter took turns cradling the two urns that contained the ashes of Kat and Brigit. Kat had succumbed to ALS on Good Friday, in 2004, and Brigit entered eternity on that Pentecost Sunday. As the van drove the ten friends past the Mediterranean, Jake whispered to his wife, "I say we cast their ashes into the sea. Plus, I am ready to get my feet in some water. I cannot believe I am so near the Mediterranean and I am not going fishing! I am having withdrawal, Terese. I am going to split from the group after the Galilee and get some time in deep water."

"That's fine with me. But relax; you will be happy when we get into the Upper Galilee. We are staying in a cabin in the woods where David lives, high in the mountains, in the village of Harashim. When we return to Jerusalem, we can drop you off near the sea. And no, we are not throwing these ashes into the sea; I want to plant them both under an olive tree when we get to that church in Cana, where the Gateway High School's Interact Club provided the funds for 500 olive trees."

Jake squeezed his wife's hand and leaned in close. "The church in Cana, where the new trees are now rooted, will be the perfect place to leave what was once Kat and Brigit. They both appreciated the fact that Jesus' first miracle happened at the wedding in Cana, when Jesus turned the water into wine and kept the party going."

Terese smiled and closed her eyes, and Jake looked out the window and thought about fishing. Jack had been introduced to Joy, a friend of Louise, who was accompanying them. Louise, the Jewish co-founder of the Olive Trees Foundation for Peace had many Jewish friends Jack was anxious to meet.

"So, tell me how a twenty-four-year-old from Nashville decides to move to Israel, where she knows no one. What made you do it, and how has it been these past seven months?"

Joy lit up as she told him, "My friends got so tired of me complaining about my political frustrations over the last election; they said, 'If you don't like it here, just leave!' I had already been considering joining the Peace Corps, and when I got turned down because of a medical problem, I explored the possibility of going to Israel. I learned about, *Aliyah*, which means 'going up,' and the deal was hard to pass by. I get fifteen hundred shekels or about thirty-six hundred dollars a year in increments to help with my expenses. I can apply for unemployment benefits after seven months, as long as I look for a job. I completed *Ulpan*, which is five hundred hours of Hebrew language immersion--five months, five hours a day, for five weeks. I get subsidized rent and just moved out of the Absorption Center Projects. All the new immigrants get room, utilities, and three meals a day for the first five months in Israel. We also receive free medical care and all the doctors here are dedicated. We can go to the university with 100 percent of the tuition paid by the government. College is much cheaper here; it's about three thousand to four thousand dollars a year. Until I am thirty years old, I can receive up to three years of education for my master's degree."

Jack wondered what he would do, if he were a young American Jew without many prospects at home.

After meeting more of Khaled's family in Majd Al Krum, the ten friends split up to be hosted by various Israeli Jews and Palestinian Muslims. Louise, Jack, Jake, and Terese got into David's van for the drive to their cabins in the woods of the village of Harashim. Jack and Jake were absorbed in the mountain vistas, but Terese was captivated by David, and did not take her attention off the tall, thin, angular man as he told his story.

"My mother is fourth-generation to this land; my father was born here while this land was still called Palestine. So, I am a forty-two-year-old Israeli-Palestinian secular Jew. In 2000, when Ariel Sharon went to the Al Aqsa Mosque and provoked the violent uprising, I cried, 'Back off, man! Enough! It is enough already!' When those young Palestinian innocents were killed, I knew I had to do something. I didn't know what, but I began by knocking on doors throughout Rosh El Aim, a Christian-Arab community. I told them I just wanted to help somehow. Mostly they thought I was crazy; many today think it, too. I drove a three hundred mile radius, knocking on doors, offering to help somehow. One day, I was sitting with a bunch of Bedouin kids, and I began tapping my fingers on my thigh. The next thing, all of these kids were imitating me, and I realized I could bring them drums. I have friends who are musicians and artisans, and they have all offered an open hand. Without any assistance from the Israeli government, we have established centers of peace/

shalom/*salaam* that offer tutoring, health care, folk dance, music lessons, and artistic projects to the least and easily forgotten. We have built community between Israeli Jews and Bedouins, and Palestinian Christians and Muslims.

"It's been five years now, and I continue to make daily rounds all the way into the Golan Heights. Many others have joined in and are keeping the projects moving forward, as I take on new ones. I have a friend named Hagit Breittman, a Jewish woman who has done the unthinkable! She opened her home to Bedouin woman, and they get together weekly to sew and, more importantly, to be a community. Right now, we are building community here, for security comes from community, not walls and gates. We absolutely have hope that one day, these Bedouin woman will travel to America with their embroidery and weaving. Hagit also started up a daily lunch service for the poor in the community. She provides food and comfort for hundreds everyday, and has done it all without government assistance.

"Today, the people are so in need of good leadership. If they can find it, they will follow. People need to be taught morals, boundaries, limits, and manners. This is the stuff Jesus taught, and he led the people. Today, people are lost in a violent cycle without basic human rights and respect for the other. Forget co-existence; we must have basic existence, basic human rights. Maybe when others see we care, they will care too." [www.shalam.org]

Terese told David, "You remind me of another socially radical Palestinian Jew who went through Galilee, offering free healings and love."

The following day, Khaled and his brother Hamid drove a ten-year-old Toyota up the long incline into the occupied Golan Heights behind David's van. The Toyota began to smoke and sputter, and the brothers pulled off to the side of the road. David turned the van around as soon as he noticed, and as he exited the van to help the brothers, he announced, "If you need to stretch your legs, don't walk off the pavement. There can be land mines anywhere the pavement ends."

After a half hour, and after three liters of water were poured into the Toyota's radiator, David led the brothers to the service station, and then they, too, crammed into the van and drove five more minutes to meet Moneer Sabagh at the elementary school where the Olive Trees Foundation for Peace had provided two thousand trees that were now thriving. Moneer was the sole founder of the Association for Improving and Developing the Family in what was once Syria, but is now the occupied Golan Heights. Moneer was a young, soft-spoken Muslim, who told them, "I am in a delicate situation. The Israeli government built our school, but the community here is occupied, and resentment runs high. I am trying to get them to care about what we have, to enrich it, so we can thereby enrich ourselves. Because they are occupied, they struggle with the question of how they can thrive under captivity. It is a difficult situation to understand--what life under occupation is about. I thank the Olive Trees Foundation for Peace for providing the trees David brought to us. We needed oaks and pines for the school campus, and we thank you for filling that need with the trees we asked for. They make a difference in the atmosphere, in the air we breathe and what we see, and in how we feel."

Saturday, June 18, 2005: Meeting with a Nobel Peace Prize Nominee

A half hour late and one or two at a time, the ten straggled into the busy office of Abouna Elias Chacour. The Melkite priest, who was a three-time Nobel nominee, a 1948 refugee, and the founder of Mars Elias Educational Institute in Ibillin, welcomed them warmly and invited them to sit around the conference table in front of his desk.

"Tell me why you have come here and what you hope to do. Then, I will share my story with you."

The youngest of the group said, "I want the win-win. I want peace for everyone, and I know it starts with every individual. I want to be the change I want to see in the world. I live in peace with everyone and I want the win-win."

Abouna Cahcour roared, "Yes, exactly! This is the only way: win-win for everyone. Anytime someone has to be right, there is oppression. With a win-win, there are always human rights. My school serves forty-five hundred interfaith children, and the criteria for employment here is an open mind and open heart for all of Abraham's sons and daughters."

Jack thought Chacour looked and spoke like an Old Testament prophet; he had a long gray beard and a huge presence, packaged in a middle-aged spread. Jack often heard music in his head; once again, it was U2:

Lay down your guns
All your daughters of Zion,
All your Abraham sons.
I don't know if I can take it,
I'm not easy on my knees.
Here's my heart; you can break it.
I need some release
Release
Release
We need Love and Peace

Love and Peace. [U2, 2004. How to Dismantle an Atomic Bomb, "Love and Peace or Else"]

Chacour mesmerized his audience. "I am a Palestinian Israeli who lives for peace and reconciliation. The problem here is not about the land. There is a blockage between Arabs and Jews. It must end. We need to explore a third way to rise above the conflict. There are three million Palestinians living in refugee camps! This injustice must come to an end. Once, we Jews and Arabs were partners and friends. The only way out of this conflict is to rise above it. You Americans are still too young! You think money and weapons solve problems! Only love and respect can do that. You reach for the moon, but not your neighbor. What we need from you Americans are smiles of hope. We need you to plant hope. We need you to visit us, so that we would know we are not alone. Do simple things, and always do them with a smile. Don't rely too much on God! You know what He wants; now, DO IT!"

Terese thought, Do something.

Sunday, June 19, 2005: Manger Square and Dashiesh Refugee Camp

Jack was intensely uncomfortable looking at the pain-filled face of the father of the seventeen-year-old altar boy who was one of three children shot in Manger Square thirty-eight days after 9/11. Not until Jack sat in the home of Johnny's father did he realize the close connection in time to their losses.

Jack could not look into Johnny's father's face, but he heard him explain, "My son was carrying his younger cousin when the IDF terminated his life. He died in my arms on the floor of the Church of the Nativity for the crime of being a Palestinian in Manger Square that day. We never thought the IDF would enter our holy ground. We were very wrong. The IDF hid on the mountain, sniped at our children, and never apologized."

Jack knew no words that would mean anything, and so, instead, slipped one hundred dollars into the father's pocket as he left. He thought to himself, This place becomes more surreal all the time. I feel like I am in a cosmic nightmare. It's some kind of holocaust hangover that is driving this madness. Too many things have not been addressed, and violence has become ordinary life. The Galilee is a different world; this trip now is now getting to me in ways I did not anticipate.

Imad Younis, the coordinator for Islamic Relief of the West Bank, had arranged for the group to meet the family of the first female suicide bomber, Ayyat Lufti Al Akhrass in her families' home in Dashieh refugee camp. Twelve thousand Palestinians with a 70 percent unemployment rate are sheltered in the one-kilometer-square-large, fifty-seven-year-old refugee camp, just minutes away from the Church of the Nativity. Jack was mystified when he entered the immaculate, yet sparse dwelling, after walking past the poverty in the streets. The group was greeted warmly by the still-grieving father, as the mother served cold coke and then hot minted tea in gold-rimmed glasses on top of silver trays.

Jack had not yet learned not to ask questions before the formalities had been attended to. He caused a moment of stress when he blurted out, "Did you know your daughter was going to blow herself up?"

After an awkward silence and a deep moan from Khaled, Ayyat Lufti's father told Jack through an interpreter, "No, I did not know anything. If I had known my daughter was going to blow herself up, I would have immediately stopped her. She did not tell anyone she was going to blow herself up on March 29, 2002. She did this on her own; nobody encouraged her. If I had known, I would have stopped her. Her action caused me to lose my job. I was the foreman in a building company in Israel. When I reported to work on the day after her death, I was told to go home; I was out of a job and haven't found another since. My daughter left a note saying she did this tragic act because she wanted to bring attention to the suffering and oppression of Palestinians, and could no longer wait for Arab armies to liberate the people. No human being wants another to die. The pressure of this occupation is forcing our children to do this. The root cause is the occupation."

Jack wrestled with asking if any Hamas members were around to talk with, but as nobody else had anything more to say, he kept his mouth shut and watched Terese's face. She was anxious to leave for Beit Jala, the west side of Bethlehem, to meet a little boy she had first seen in an American Catholic newspaper five years before. Four-year-old George had been captured on film the morning after his bedroom had been destroyed by Israeli gunfire the night before. The IDF flew American-made Apache helicopters over the peaceful Christian village in retaliation for the action of some militants who had infiltrated in to snipe across the street a few miles away into the Jewish settlement. A four-foot hole was blown into George's bedroom with shrapnel that read, MADE IN U.S.A.

Terese had clipped the photo of George as soon as she saw it, placed it in an antique frame, and set it on the table, where she lit candles and then thought about people in need. Every time she looked in George's eyes, she heard her heart say, "Do something."

When Khaled had first told Jake and Terese he was planning the Olive Trees for Peace trip to Israel and Palestine, she knew she wanted to go and find George. Through well-placed friends and the Internet, he was located, and the ten descended on the family, who lived in Beit Jala, just before sundown. George was now in the fourth grade, shy, and withdrawn. He, his mother, and sister all still suffered post-traumatic stress syndrome from the night when U.S.-made bombs blew open the wall in front of George's empty bed. He had been hiding in his parent's room and fainted when he heard the boom that came from the room he had just left. Terese felt badly for intruding on the family and wished she hadn't come to them. Then George looked at her sideways, smiled the smile of an unscathed child, and whispered, "I like you."

George's father spoke while fighting back tears. "There was absolutely no gunfire coming from our side of the neighborhood. None at all--it was quiet here. We are not bitter, and although the government never apologized, we forgive, but it is still very hard."

Jack thought, This is what my government calls collateral damage.

Afterwards, the Deputy Mayor of Bethlehem met the group in the empty lobby of the Hotel Bethlehem. George Sa'adeh, softly spoken and articulate, told the group, "The occupation is the reason that many highly educated Christians are leaving the Holy Land. There is no opportunity here. Three hundred fifty thousand residents have left their homes in Bethlehem since 2000. My people are leaving for better jobs, justice, and basic human rights. In 1948, Christians were 20 percent of the total population in the Holy Land. Today, they are less than 1.5 percent, and they continue to migrate because of the occupation, oppression, lack of opportunity, and denial of basic human rights. Add in the low birth weight, and one day soon, there may be no Christian witness in this land. One day, all the churches here could be nothing more than museums. I lost my own daughter in an ambush. I was driving the same car model as the one the IDF Special Forces were looking for. They shot first and asked questions after. My daughter Christine lost her life. The government has never apologized."

Tuesday in Hebron with Jerry Levin

Jack and Terese met Jerry at the Bethlehem Hotel for the daytrip to Hebron. Jerry Levin, full-time volunteer with Christian Peacemaker Teams (CPT) had been filing Internet reports, and both Jack and Terese had been reading them.

Jerry had been CNN's Middle East bureau chief in the 1980s, and a secular Jew. He was captured and held hostage in Lebanon by the Hezbollah for nearly a year, experienced a mystical Christmas Eve, and was never the same.

Jack was already mopping his brow from the heat by 7:30 a.m., but Jerry never sweated. Lightly built and sprouting bilateral hearing aids, he told them, "Every time I get ready to return to Palestine, everyone asks me, 'Aren't you afraid?' I reply, 'Of what, the Palestinians? No way! But when it comes to the Israelis soldiers, you bet I am!'"

Hebron is where 450 Israeli settlers are protected by three thousand IDF. The eighteen- to twenty-one-year-olds patrol the streets with Uzis at the ready and turned the trio away at a checkpoint. Jerry informed them, "Most of the soldiers don't like the CPTs. Whenever they won't let us through, we just go another way, and always, eventually, get where we want to go."

Terese was nauseated the entire day. Jack kept getting hotter. "This is nuts! This is insane! These narrow, winding stone streets have been here for centuries. Now, one side of the way is all Israeli, and the other is Palestinian. Their only connection to the other is this thick, yet deeply sagging netting above my head. I cannot believe the huge rocks, shovels, electronic equipment, furniture, and all manner of debris that have been flung on it! I wonder if I will be underneath it when it gives way."

Jerry smiled and told him, "It gets cleaned out about every year or so. Come back in a few months, and this netting will be much closer to your head. The settlers just throw whatever they want onto the netting; they do whatever they want and get away with it. The CPTs run interference by nonviolent resistance; we get the children and woman to where they need to be going and back again. Sometimes, the settlers curse and stone us all; it keeps it interesting."

Jerry pointed out all the empty and formerly Palestinian homes that the settlers had painted graffiti and Stars of David on. Both Terese and Jack could not believe it when they saw, spray painted on a now empty, but formerly Palestinian home, "GAS THE ARABS."

Jack mumbles, "I feel like I have entered into every movie set and photograph I have ever seen of the ghettos the Jews were forced into before the Holocaust."

Terese wanted to visit inside the Abraham mosque, and an Arab guide was found who spoke a little English. She put on the brown prayer shawl, but couldn't hide the fact she was an American. Immediately, she was followed by an inquisitive young mother, adolescents, and small children, who kept laughing and staring at her. Terese thought it was the way she pronounced "*Marhaba* (hello) and *Salaam* (peace)" that made them laugh and want to follow along. Before the tour was through, the guide was able to ascertain that the family now lived in the mosque ever since the husband had died, but the cause of death remained unstated. Terese and the family took a picture together, while everyone said, "*Salaam.*"

After the long day in Hebron, and then back to Bethlehem, Jerry walked Jack and Terese through the checkpoint that leads to Jerusalem. Terese was mesmerized by the watchtower and barbed wire, until she stared into the eyes of the youth who checked her passport while cradling an Uzi like a baby. She wondered, "How would I endure if I had to live here? What would I be like?

What would my kids be like if they had to serve in this military and spend all day checking paperwork? What would they be like if they were the ones handing over their paperwork?"

Jack couldn't shut up. "This is incredible; walking through the checkpoints are facts on the ground that tour buses never experience. It is two different worlds kept from the other, tourists and Palestinians. The feeling of oppression is visceral; you miss it if you only pass by in tour busses with Israeli license plates. This situation reminds me of what it was like in America before Martin Luther King. Something has got to give; this situation is untenable, and so is Vanunu's. You're the only source of information I have read in America, except for a TV documentary I caught on the History Channel, entitled 'Sexpionage.' But, if it hadn't been for your reports, I would never have known about his release last April and three arrests since."

"I haven't spoken with Mordechai in a few months now. Give him a call, I can give you his cell phone number; he appreciates being treated to dinner or a beer."

In the taxi back to Jerusalem, Jack remembered reading an interview on St. Patrick's Day, which quoted Vanunu speaking to the media after he had been arrested specifically for speaking to the media, and Jack had been impressed. Vanunu said, "I have no more secrets to tell and have not set foot in Dimona for more than eighteen years. I have been out of prison, although not free, for one year now. Despite the illegal restrictions on my speech, I have again and again spoken out against the use of nuclear weapons anywhere and by any nation. I have given away no sensitive secrets, because I have none. I have not acted against the interests of Israel, nor do I wish to. I have been investigated by the police again and again, and re-arrested. They have found nothing. I have done nothing but speak for peace and world safety from a nuclear disaster. I do not want to harm Israel, but rather, to warn of an enormous danger. I want to work for world peace and the abolition of nuclear weapons. I want the human race to survive."

From reading Jerry Levin's Internet reports on Vanunu, Jack knew that he was still not allowed to leave the country, to speak to foreigners, to go to Palestinian territories, nor to approach a foreign embassy. Although released from Ashkelon on April 21, 2004, he had been arrested three more times. He had been charged with "attempting to leave the country," for riding in a taxi to go the few miles from Jerusalem to Bethlehem for Christmas Eve mass in 2004.

The Israeli government had imposed the draconian Emergency Defense Regulations of the British Mandate upon Vanunu. Jack struggled, trying to understand how a democracy could get away with regulations that suspend the rights of individuals to speak freely and move about. The Emergency Defense

Regulations were implemented first by Britain against both Palestinians and Jews after World War II. Articles 109, 110, and 120 give power to the government to enter anyone's home at any hour, day or night, and remove anything they want. On November 11, 2004, thirty armed officers stormed into Vanunu's room while he was having morning coffee, and they confiscated his computer and letters. They have yet to be returned.

"When the Jewish community was suffering under the atrocious regulations, which were used by the British against both Palestinians and Jews after World War II, a leading Jewish lawyer, Yaccov Shapiro, who later became Israel's minister of justice, described the Regulations as "unparalleled in any civilized country; there were no such laws in Nazi Germany." [Naim Ateek; Justice and Only Justice, page 34-35].

The next morning, Jack took a cab to Ramallah and saw the Wall in full frontal, brutal view. On his left was twenty feet of abominable concrete; on his right, there were rows of bankrupt businesses. Jack wondered how many U.S. tax dollars were spent on the abomination.

David, from the Upper Galilee, popped into Jack's mind. "Back off, man; it's enough; back off!" Jack thought the same about the wall, and then got lost in thought until his cab pulled into the Palestinian Authority's compound, where Arafat had been held captive and is buried now. Jack was amused at the reception he received from the soldiers when he arrived at the Headquarters. Nobody asked for any ID or to look in his briefcase.

"This is surreal; the IDF carry these huge Uzis, and the PA's guns look like toys," Jack commented.

Tony responded. "They often don't even work." Tony Nassar had made the arrangements for Jack to interview President Abbas's chief of staff and met him at the gate. Tony was a law student and paralegal at the law firm President Abbas used for personal business. Jack had made contact with Tony through the Palestinian Christian Yahoo Group. Tony was twenty-four years old and supported his widowed mother and young sister without a thought for himself. He told Jack that although most of the family had already moved to America, he would never leave Palestine.

Jack was ten minutes early for his appointment with Rafiq Husseini, chief of staff to President Abbas. An unnamed soldier escorted Jack to the conference room and another brought cool water and hot tea. A moment later, Dr. Husseini greeted Jack with a warm smile and told him, "We have lost more than 1.1 million fruit-bearing trees in Palestinian territories. Trees are about food, the environment, and life. Ancient trees have been demolished by tanks, and we thank the Olive Trees Foundation for Peace for addressing the need to replace them and rebuild the faith of our people. Palestine has always been tolerant to people of all religions. The Jews came here out of Spain along with many Arabs--and then came Zionism. When one wants to take over another, war happens. President Abbas is a very bad politician; he does not lie! He is ready to move on from the past. We have quit crying over our losses; we must move on. Live and let live is the motto of this administration. We can not carry on a battle; it must stop. Peace can only happen with peace, not force. President Abbas has promised, 'We will do whatever it takes to show the world we want peace.' We need America to help us. The best thing would be for Americans to come and see the truth of the situation for themselves. I encourage Americans to come and see the Wall; it has nothing to do with security, but everything to do with grabbing water and more land. When Americans understand the real situation, things will change for the better. The humiliation at the checkpoints is beyond belief. It can drive anyone to desperation. We condemn all terrorism, but resisting occupation is necessary."

That night, Jack walked through the checkpoint from Ramallah to catch a cab back to the Ambassador Hotel. He cringed when he saw the watchtower's small window lit up, and considered how easy it would be to be shot at. The ground was rocky, uneven, and littered with debris. Jack's crepitus arthritic knees crackled more than usual as he navigated the uneven ground, and he thought, Thank God for that full moon; at least there's a little light in this darkness. How do old people get around in this environment? I imagine there must be a lot of broken hips, or else they never leave their homes.

Jack's passport was investigated by a dull-eyed female with boredom etched deep in her young face, and he wondered, What am I going to do with all I have seen and heard? These experiences can't just be for me alone, but what am I going to do with them?

The next day, Jack met Mordechai Vanunu at a seafood restaurant. As soon as they ordered, Jack asked, "So, what was your childhood like?"

Vanunu thought for a long time before he responded. "It was normal--it was normal--it was normal."

"What is normal?"

"I was born in Marrakesh, on October 13, 1954. I was the second oldest of eleven; the first seven of us migrated from Morocco in 1963 after the Zionists came and convinced the neighborhood that Israel was the Promised Land. Instead of the land of milk and honey, we were banished to the desert of Beersheba."

"Wait, I have never been to Marrakesh; tell me about it."

"Did you ever see that Doris Day movie, *The Man Who Knew Too Much*?"

"Is that the one where she sings 'Que sera, sera'?"

"That's the one. The beginning is exactly where I grew up. I was about eight years old when I would wander all over the bazaar all by myself. I had a few friends at school, but always went to the bazaar alone. I preferred to be alone to observe; I was always watching everyone. I was always alone, but never lonely. We lived in a small neighborhood of Melah. It was a few hundred years old, with a wall and a gate just like the Old City. Some people painted their homes many colors, and the streets were narrow and had no names. I remember this very tall, black Muslim Arab, who would fill a sheepskin with water from the town well. He would carry it around his neck and sell water to those who did not want to fetch it themselves. My father ran a successful grocery store, and my mother was a seamstress. She would see a picture of a dress in a magazine and then would copy it for herself. My mother's family had moved to Israel in 1956, and they sent me and my sisters and brothers clothes and things. We also got support from JOINT, a Jewish organization from the United States that sent us jeans and boots."

"Did you have fun?"

"It was fun to watch the gymnasts perform at the bazaar; I would watch them for hours. I wouldn't go home until after dark, and we lived in an apartment quadrangle. There were four families on each of the two floors, and we shared the rooftop and courtyard. There was no electricity, no running water, and no sewer. My very first memory is of when I was four years old and my mother had to run downstairs for a while. She told me to keep an eye on my newborn sister, and as soon as I was alone, I found out the difference between girls and boys. I was still four years old when I began wondering, What is above the sky? What is the end of the end?

"I grew up in an Orthodox Jewish home, but rejected it all by the eighth grade. When I went to the University, I became an existentialist…. When I was eight years old I stole some money for the first and last time. My father would take my older brother Al and I to his grocery store whenever we weren't in school. Al would always go into the back and play with boxes, but I stayed up front, and listened and learned. One Friday afternoon, my father told me to watch the register, as he had to run out somewhere. There was one hundred shekels in the money box, and I put it in my pocket as soon as he left. When he returned, the first thing he did was look into the box, and then he asked me, 'Where is the money? Did you take it?'

"I saw no way out and, in my panic, I lied and said something stupid. 'No no, I didn't take it; go ahead and check my pocket.' He did, and he found the money and began to beat me with a belt. He wounded me a little in my head. That was the day I learned not to steal, but it was not until the next day when I learned not to lie. The next day at school, the teacher demanded that we all uncover our heads. When I did, the teacher saw my wound, and he sent me to the principal, who asked, 'What happened to you?' I didn't want to admit that my father beat me, so I told him some Arabs had beaten me up. He called the police and my lie made a lot of trouble for some innocent guys, and I have never lied since then."

"So, you were always a good boy?"

"Yes, I was a good student and stayed out of trouble."

"Have you always been stubborn?"

Vanunu thought for a very long time. "When I was thirteen years old, I got mad at my parents and decided I would punish them. I began my first hunger strike and it lasted three days. My parents acted like they didn't care, and it was not until I got very weak that I got their attention. I also remember getting really mad at my mother before a Jewish holiday. I had new clothes I wanted to wear on Friday night, but she insisted that I wait until the next day. We locked horns, but she had the power and won in the end. I fumed the entire evening."

"So, this was when you had been in Israel for about five years?"

"Yes, in 1963 the Zionists came to my village and encouraged everyone to migrate to Israel. There was no family discussion; my father just told us we were leaving, and six months later, we boarded the train to Casablanca and got on a World War II military ship. The ship kept going up and down, and everyone was crammed into an open space; people everywhere kept throwing up. After four days, we arrived in Marseilles. This was a great place, but we had to leave for Israel. The next boat was bigger and modern, and the journey was smoother. When we arrived in Israel, the Interior Minister assigned us to Beersheba, but all the rest of our family had been assigned to Nazareth, and we wanted to go there, too. We had no choice, and home was a small hut in the desert. There was nothing in it and we had nothing much with us. After a few days, my mother left for Nazareth; it was chaos, and we had nothing to do to occupy us. Outside, there was only desert, but I walked a few hours everyday so I could be in the Old City. I started exploring around a Mexican-looking town, never talking with anyone, but always watching everyone. Three weeks later, my mother returned, and then my uncle, Joseph, arrived and took us up north to see some more newly arrived family. We stayed for two months, and then moved into a new apartment in Beersheba. I went to the fifth grade and met a few friends, but they were strange people. They were Romanians and a lot of Middle Easterners, who used bad language and seemed cheap to me. Even the school supplies were inferior to those I had had in Morocco. Even the ice cream was not ice cream; it was just ice, and there was no Pepsi. I didn't like it at all, and wondered why I had to be there. There were only Jewish people around; I never saw an Arab or Palestinian then, and the old mosque was uninhabited. My mother had babies every two years. I preferred to be alone, but I was never lonely. Even when I walked with my father on Saturday to pray, I didn't talk, but I wondered about God and truth. My father became even more orthodox as I turned away. I couldn't accept all the teachings and decided I would not accept any of them. At fourteen years old, I began to doubt, and by sixteen, I left Judaism for good. I didn't know if God even existed, and I didn't even care. I decided I would decide for myself what is good and what is bad; I didn't need anyone telling me the rules. For me, it was about doing to others what I wanted them to do to me; I didn't need any other rule. I was sent to Yeshiva, the Jewish boarding school in the Old City. I experienced a great disconnect from God. I didn't talk to anyone about any of it. I kept everything within and continued to wonder about finding my way, my direction, and the purpose of my life. I have always searched for answers. I kept my mouth shut about not following the faith and excelled in secular studies. With everything else, I just went through the motions--in the eleventh grade, two friends and I were listening to the radio. It is a big sin and crime to use electricity on the Sabbath. The rabbi caught us and called my father to come get me, and when we had almost reached our house, I smelled that he was going to beat me, so I ran the five meters back to school without looking back. The next day, the rabbi sent me for an intensive week of Jewish studies. I was angry for the entire week. After that, I returned back to my boarding room. My two friends and I had become outcasts; we were forever ignored by the other students. The isolation became very comfortable, and I began walking in the desert alone every night without any fear. I would just walk around and imagine that I would find my way, and have some success."

The Army and Leaving Israel

"I passed all my classes except for English and Hebrew studies. At eighteen years old, I had my mind and health checked by the Israeli army doctors and was assigned to be a pilot. But I failed the hand-eye coordination test and was assigned to the Navy, instead. Three weeks later, they sent me to the Engineering Unit, where I learned about land mines, bridges, and explosives. I started training with fifty others and was the most unenthusiastic of the bunch. I stood back from it all and saw it as if it were just playing stupid games. Mostly, everyone else was serious, but I just didn't care; all I could see was the futility. The day I left home for the service, my mother walked me to the bus. She gave me all the Jewish stuff--you know, the phylacteries? The leather straps for the head and left arm? I put it all aside until I got my first leave, and then I returned it all home and never said a word about it. I never spoke with my parents about rejecting their faith. When I was in prison, my mother came to me and told me that I was suffering because I was a Christian. I know I caused them a lot of pain, and they have suffered because of my case. I forgive them, even though they rejected me and my Christian faith. I have always thought for myself and made up my own mind. As a young boy, I thought too many of the rules of Judaism were of no use—like the rule that says you can't mix meat and cheese together. Well, the first time I did, nothing happened, so then I began turning on the lights on Saturday. I tried to experience everything that had been forbidden. That first Yom Kippur I didn't fast, didn't pray, and felt totally free for the first time in my life."

"Ok, so did you start having fun?"

"No, still no fun, but I finally met some secular Jews, traveled freely as a soldier, and served in the occupied territories near Bethlehem. I would make treks of fifteen miles through villages, and I felt how poor the people were under occupation and how they suffered without reason, except for the reason of injustice. In the 1970s, Israel built many fortresses and spent lots of money on equipment, but nothing on the people I saw, who were oppressed and under occupation. I got really mad and upset every time I thought about how much money they wasted, but I kept my mouth shut and kept it all to myself. After a year, I finished my training and was assigned to train more soldiers. For me it was all futility and waste; I saw these children become soldiers and thought, What a complete waste. When the Yom Kippur War broke out, I was home on leave. I returned the next day to my station near Ramallah. Soldiers with less than a month of training got called to go with me to the Jordan Valley. There weren't enough trained troops, and we were lucky we didn't see any fighting and got to return to base after three days. After a few months, we all went to Syria and the Golan Heights. When Kissinger coordinated the ceasefire, the Israeli army destroyed the area before leaving there. I was promoted to First Sergeant, and they wanted me to re-up. I said no.

"I began my studies at Tel Aviv University when I was twenty-one. I studied physics until the army called me up for thirty days' reserve service. When I returned to school, I couldn't catch up. I worked in a bakery at night and attended class all day. This was the first time I met Palestinians as human beings. I began attending political demonstrations inside the university. It was all about equal human rights and respecting all others. By the time I was twenty-three, I began working at the Dimona. It was suppose to be a textile plant, but I was hired for the control room. At the time, I had no idea what it was in control of.

"I really didn't even want the job; I tried to get them not to hire me. On the application, they asked if I knew any Palestinians. As I had an acquaintance, I said yes, hoping it would disqualify me from employment. They accepted me anyway. I watched them as closely as they watched me. I began studying philosophy and geography, and read literature."

"Did you listen to music? Did you know the Beatles and Bob Dylan?"

"Sure, but I prefer classical. And I began wondering more about life and politics. I decided to become a hermit and vegetarian. I lived alone, but never was lonely. It wasn't ever fun, but I enjoy the quiet. I was never sad, but never happy, either. After a year, I got bored with the routine job at the Dimona and wanted to leave. I went to Beersheba University and studied economics for a year. I became involved in university politics and in student unions. I was all about protecting Palestinian students' rights. I sided with Palestinians more and more, and was invited to help establish a group of Palestinian and Jewish students for peace and justice. This was also the time I found out that it was dangerous for me to speak the truth. I was being watched, but I continued to express myself anyway. After six months, I got called in by security at the Dimona, and they asked me, 'Can you imagine why you are here?'

"I answered, 'My university activity?' They then questioned me about all my contacts and told me to stop, because I was in danger. I told them I would try, but I knew I would continue on, because it was the right cause and I would not hide my thoughts.

"After five months, they called me in again and demanded that I stop my activities. A few months later, the chief security man took me to the Tel Aviv Secret Room, where the Israeli army security officer grilled me. They told me I could get fifteen years in prison if I didn't stop my university activities. I left the meeting and walked to a Palestinian bookstore, knowing they were watching me. That night, I wrote in my diary, '1/85. I should have finished this job at Dimona before now. Time to quit.'

"I finished the university with a BA in philosophy and geography, and made plans to leave Israel and begin a new life in America. In August of 1985, I was put on a list of people who should be dismissed from the Dimona. They were laying off 10 percent, but when they told me I was going, I confronted them with 'Why are you dismissing me? I am a good worker; you are getting rid of me for political reasons, aren't you?' The union protected me, and after two months, they told me they were transferring me to a less secure area.

"I told them I would stay where I was, or else I would resign. They said, 'Okay, resign.' And I did. I had already shot the two rolls of film. I worked the night shift and had lots of time alone. I found the keys to the restricted areas in the shower room. I left the film in my locker for a few days before taking it out of the Dimona. I knew they were watching me. I left Israel in January of 1986, and went to search for someone to share my story with. I didn't develop the film until six months later. I was waiting until I found a newspaper that would cover the story. I met a Canadian author on my way to Greece, but nothing came of it. I traveled to Athens, Bangkok, and then went to Russia. I was thirty years old in a Moscow hotel, wondering if I should tell my story to the Red Army. I decided to leave, instead. The reason I had arrived there was that before I left the Dimona, I had checked out the Palestinian Communist Party to see how the communists worked. I was curious and wondered if they would help me once I left Israel. But when I witnessed the poverty and nothing but military cars everywhere, I decided to get out of there.

"I went to the Far East and met some people who had run away from Chernobyl, and I told them about the Dimona. Two weeks later I arrived in Sydney and stayed for six months. I went to St. John Anglican church and became friends with the people I met there. I got a job driving a taxi and met a freelance journalist named Gervevo; I told him my story, and he was enthusiastic to help me get it out. He thought I wanted to make money on it, but I told him I just wanted to prevent a nuclear war and contribute to a positive change in the Middle East. Then I met Peter Hounam."

Baptism by Fire

"I really had no clue what I was doing by getting baptized a Christian; I just felt like I had to do it. It was my way to become a new being. It wasn't until after my trial that I started to read the New Testament. While I was in prison, I would read aloud for a half hour, twice a day. I would read the entire New Testament and begin it again when I finished the Book of Revelation. I did this for myself, as well as for my captors--not so much the prison guards, but the ones who watched me on camera twenty-four hours a day. Once I covered up the camera that spied on me and was punished with one month in solitary, without any books or radio; no contact with anyone anywhere was allowed. It was just them, watching me, constantly watching me."

"Who are they?"

"The *Shen Beet*, you know, like the FBI and the *Mossad*, like your CIA—they were watching me. They tortured me by keeping a light on in my cell constantly for two years. They told me it was because they were afraid I would commit suicide, and the oppressive camera was for my safety. They recruited the guards and other prisoners to irritate me. They would deprive me of sleep by making loud noises near my cell all night long.

"I chose to read them 1 Corinthians 13: 4-8, instead:

Love is patient, love is kind. It does not envy, it does not boast, it is not proud. It is not rude, it is not self-seeking, it is not easily angered, and it keeps no record of wrongs. Love does not delight in evil but rejoices with THE TRUTH! It always protects, it always trusts, always hopes, and always perseveres. Love never fails.

"For the first five years, twice a day I would loudly pray by reading Bible verses. I would also read the Anglican service from the *Book of Common Prayer*. I did it twice a day, everyday, for five years. I began to see I had become like a machine. I knew if I continued I would lose my mind. So after that, I only prayed in silence. Although I knew I was driving them nuts with my loud praying, it was driving me nuts, too. I changed my routine. I was allowed outside every day for two hours; I had been jogging around in circles for the two hours, but now I changed my routine. I began to alter that and all my routines so I would not be like a machine. I refused to eat when they brought my food in. I would decide everyday what time I would eat and what I would eat. I chose a different time everyday to do anything. The camera was there to learn my behavior so they could manipulate me. I knew I had to constantly change my routine. I began reading more books about health, nutrition, history, philosophy, and literature, and kept my prayer life quiet."

"When you were baptized in Sydney, just a few months before you were abducted and tried, you took the name John Crossman. Was that because of St. John of the Cross and his *The Dark Night of The Soul?*

"I haven't read him."

"Not many have, and even fewer understand what he was talking about. John of the Cross was a Spanish poet and mystic who wrote about the contemplative life and the divine union of the soul with God in this life. He was an ardent disciple of Theresa of Avilla's reforms, which greatly agitated the church hierarchy during the time of the Spanish Inquisition. He received a great deal of abuse for his thoughts and spent a lot of time in prison, writing."

Vanunu went silent again. Jack wondered if he stirred up too many bad memories, but asked, "Tomorrow is my last day before I fly home to upstate New York. Now I have to get to Notre Dame for the Interfaith Peace Conference. Will you take a hike with me up to the Mount of Olives tomorrow evening and tell me exactly how you became a Christian?"

Vanunu agreed, and Jack paid the tab, said goodbye, and walked to Notre Dame Cathedral for the satellite-linked interfaith conference for peace. Dan Rather moderated from D.C. as Jack sat in the audience in Jerusalem. The interfaith panel comprised moderates attempting to reclaim the battlefield of ideas from extremists on both sides. Rev. Theodore Hessburgh, president emeritus of the University of Notre Dame began the evening with a pledge: "The peace of the world begins in Jerusalem."

Dr. Tsvia Walden, of the board of directors of the Peres Center and Geneva Initiative, offered a plan: "There is a need for a third party in the negotiations that could enable both sides to trust each other. There are more people in this region interested in making concessions; they all want peace so desperately."

The coordinator of World Bank emergency services to the PA, Rania Kharma, commented, "We all need to be the bridges to our leaders and carry the message that only justice, equality, and human rights will bring peace. Give people justice, and they will reward you with peace."

Sheik Imad Falouiji warned, "Religions must go back to their origins. God commands us to love each other and live together. This Holy Land was given to all people. This land is on fire. There is an occupation that musty be removed. The language of peace cannot succeed without justice for all."

Jack remembered President Bush's second inaugural promise: "In the long run, there is no justice without freedom, and there can be no human rights without liberty...All who live in tyranny and hopelessness can know the United States will not ignore your oppression or excuse your oppressors. When you stand for liberty, we will stand with you."

The bishop of Jerusalem, Rt. Rev. Riah Abu Assal, recaptured Jack's attention as he stated, "Peace is an act. Blessed are the peacemakers, not the peace talkers. Peace is possible in the Holy Land. The root cause for the lack of peace since 1967 is the occupation. For peace to make progress in the Middle East, we need to deal with the root cause. Religion was not meant to bring death. All those involved in searching for peace should commit themselves to work for justice and truth."

After the conference, Jack walked alone to the Ambassador Hotel and wondered, These past fifteen days have changed me. I learned more in this short time through experience than from years of reading. I don't know what I am going to do with this knowledge, and I don't have a clue if You want me to do anything at all. But, it is the words of Thomas Merton that keep coming back to me:

> Oh God, I have no idea where I am going. I do not see the road ahead of me. I cannot know for certain where it will end. Nor do I really know myself, and the fact that I think I am following your will does not necessarily mean that I actually am. But I believe that the desire to please you does in fact please you. I hope I have that desire in all that I am doing. I hope I will never do anything apart from that desire. And I know that if I do this you will always lead me by the right road, although I may know nothing about it... and I will not fear."
> [Thomas Merton, Thoughts in Solitude, pg.79]

The next morning, Jack met Sami and George at the Bethlehem office of the Holy Land Trust and learned more about their education and training for all segments of Palestinian society, and about how direct nonviolent action against the occupation is done. He learned about the Holy Land Trust's many opportunities to participate in fact-finding missions and travel encounters to meet Jews, Christians, and Muslims working together for peace and justice. Jack took a picture with Sami in front of a poster that looked, at first glance, to be an eye chart, but read, "END THE OCCUPATION."

Jack asked Sami for a poster of his own, and told him, "I am already planning on attending TIKKUN's teach–in to Congress next year on Israel and Palestine. I think I will take this eye chart with me and see how good the eyes of Congress are."

That afternoon, Jack met Rev. Attek at the Sabeel office, but Jack did most of the talking. "I have been reading the Sabeel Documents about morally responsible investment and nonviolent response to the occupation. This is exactly what we American Christians should be discussing, instead of continuing the debate over the mystery of love and marriage. Surely everyone knows Bishop Robinson isn't the first gay bishop; he's just the first honest gay bishop. What we really need to seriously consider is where we lay down our money, and who we really serve. Just this morning, I read an Internet report from one segment of your opposition on the divestment issue vilifying you. Money talks and you have really hit a nerve--good job, Reverend."

Rev. Ateek smiled and shrugged as he autographed Jack's worn copy of *Justice And Only Justice.*

At 5:40 p.m., Jack met Vanunu at the American Colony. They both walked as fast as any New Yorker and maintained silence. It was not until they had scaled the high hill and the stoned tombs of many Jews came into view that Vanunu spoke. "Those are the Jews expecting to be resurrected first when the Messiah comes."

Jack retorted, "When I was in rehab, I got hold of a very bad book. It was called *Left Behind.* What got left behind was the gospel of peace and love. These books are bad theology and poor literature. Did you know that in America there are Christians who actually want Armageddon? They believe they will escape the nuclear holocaust because they are now the new chosen ones. They think they will be raptured; they think they will be lifted out of the world. They believe a theology of escapism and they ignore that Christ promised that 'The peacemakers shall be called the children of God' and that Jesus is the Prince of Peace."

Vanunu replied, "The time has come for the United States to see the truth of Zionism. It began as a secular nationalist movement, not a religious one. Then some Christians believed that when Israel became a nation, it was the beginning of the second coming. They are deluded if they believe peace will come through atomic weapons. Atomic weapons are holocaust weapons. Christians should be the first people against them. The Christians in America should be helping the Christians here. America needs to wake up to this fallacy that Jesus will come back by nuclear war. America needs to wake up to the fact that the Palestinian Christians here have no human rights. Aren't Christians supposed to be concerned about other Christians? Aren't Christians supposed to be concerned about all the poor and oppressed?"

Jack had become agitated. "It is non-negotiable: all of that stuff Jesus said about doing for the least and the oppressed. It is non-negotiable for Christians; we must forgive our enemies, and we must love those who hate us. Whatever we do or do not do, we do it unto God. Every time I went through a checkpoint, saw the wall, or heard a story of oppression, I wondered how God can stand this situation. I can't."

At the summit of the Mount of Olives, there is a lot of pavement, but not many trees. Jack found one cradling a few stone steps and sat down while Vanunu wandered about. When Vanunu appeared, Jack immediately asked, "How was it--being crucified for telling the truth?"

"My human rights have been denied me because I am a Christian. When I was on trial, I was treated just like a Palestinian: no human rights at all, and cruel and unusual punishment, all because I told the truth. The government spread slander about me, that I was a homosexual, that I hated Jews, that I wanted fame and money. What I did was sacrifice my life for the truth. In prison, I really began to feel like Jesus and Paul. When Jesus threw the money changers out of the temple, it was like me in Dimona, exposing the Israelis' dirty secrets. I felt like Paul, being thrown in prison for speaking the truth.

"The only real way to worship is in loving one's enemies. It was not easy to love my tormentors; it was only because I felt so much like Jesus crucified on the cross, and as if I was crucified in prison, that I could do it. It was not ever easy. I have forgiven but not forgotten anything, and I never will. In Israel, a life sentence is twenty-five years. Even murderers go free after seventeen. They imposed the same restrictions on me that Palestinians receive: no human rights at all; no phone; no visitors, except family, and only through an iron grill; no vacation; no holidays; and no gifts. Even murderers get out for vacations! I was locked up for eighteen years and still cannot go on vacation; I cannot leave, and that is all I am asking for, just to leave here. For eighteen years in prison, they even attempted to control my thoughts on paper. I would write exactly what I wanted and they would censor words like *kidnapped* and *atomic bomb*. They would show me how they chopped up my letters, but I continued to write exactly what I wanted. They held my body, but never my spirit or mind."

Jack asked tentatively, "Have you ever considered the idea that the anti-Christ may not be a man at all? I keep thinking how nuclear weapons are promoted by governments as instruments of peace, but they only bring destruction. I can't imagine that God intended for man to blow up this planet, but instead, to learn how to share it."

"The only way to peace is peace; the only way is nonviolence. The only answer to Israeli nuclear weapons, their aggression, occupation and oppression, and the wall and refugee camps is to answer them with truth and a peaceful voice. When I became the spy for the world, I did it all for the people of the world. If governments do not report the truth, and if the media does not report the truth, then all we can do is follow our consciences. Daniel Ellsberg did, the woman from Enron did, and I did. The United States needs to wake up and see the truth that Israel is not a democracy, unless you are a Jew. Israel is the only country in the Middle East where America can right now find WMDs. America can also find where basic human rights have been denied Christians: right here in Israel."

"In America, we are assured inalienable rights. That means they are God-given rights that governments cannot take away, such as the right to worship where and how we choose. When I read that you were not allowed to go the few miles on Christmas Eve to celebrate mass at the Church of the Nativity, I wondered, what kind of democracy is that? I cannot understand how a democracy could haul anyone to jail because they wanted to go to a church in the next town. American democracy ensures citizens the right to think and to speak out the truth as we see it. American democracy understands that everyone has the right to a life and to liberty--which means freedom from captivity and any arbitrary controls. Last night, at the Interfaith Conference, I remembered what President Bush promised at his second inauguration, and wondered if he had thought about Palestinians when he delivered it. He promised, 'There is no justice without freedom. There can be no human rights without liberty...All who live in tyranny and hopelessness can know the United States will not ignore your oppression, or excuse your oppressors. When you stand for liberty, we will stand with you.'"

The men went silent as they descended the Mount of Olives, and then climbed up three flights to a rooftop restaurant where they served the fish with skeleton and head intact, and fries on the side. After a while, Vanunu spoke and blew Jack's mind.

"Did you know that President Kennedy tried to stop Israel from building atomic weapons? In 1963, he forced Prime Minister Ben Guirion to admit the Dimona was not a textile plant, as the sign outside proclaimed, but a nuclear plant. The Prime Minister said, 'The nuclear reactor is only for peace.' Kennedy insisted on an open internal inspection. He wrote letters demanding that Ben Guirion open up the Dimona for inspection. The French were responsible for the actual building of the Dimona. The Germans gave the money; they were feeling guilty for the Holocaust, and tried to pay their way out. Everything inside was written in French, when I was there, almost twenty years ago. Back then, the Dimona descended seven floors underground. In 1955, Perez and Guirion met with the French to agree they would get a nuclear reactor if they fought against Egypt to control the Sinai and Suez Canal. That was the war of 1956. Eisenhower demanded that Israel leave the Sinai, but the reactor plant deal continued on. Kennedy demanded inspections. When Johnson became president, he made an agreement with Israel that two senators would come every year to inspect. Before the senators would visit, the Israelis would build a wall to block the underground elevators and stairways. From 1963 to '69, the senators came, but they never knew about the wall that hid the rest of the Dimona from them. Nixon stopped the inspections and agreed to ignore the situation. As a result, Israel increased production. In 1986, there were over two hundred bombs. Today, they may have enough plutonium for ten bombs a year. Who knows?"

The two walked back to St. George's Cathedral without speaking, then said goodbye at the gate. Jack continued on in the dark, alone and silent.

CHAPTER 12 :

THE REVOLUTION HAS BEGUN...

The Revolution starts now, when you rise above your fear

and tear the walls round you down.

--Steve Earle

ON WEDNESDAY, JULY 20, 2005, in Berkeley, California, Jack intuitively sensed opportunity blowing in the wind as he rounded the corner from Durant and Telegraph on his way to UC Berkeley's MLK student union building for TIKKUN's first annual conference on spiritual activism. As he crossed Bancroft Way, a young, beatifically-smiling latte-skinned youth handed him an electric green slip of paper announcing, "Compassionate Caregivers: Medical Cannabis. Two locations, 8 a.m. to 8 p.m., seven days a week."

Jack mused, "Now that my third anti-inflammatory has been pulled, I can't do narcotics in moderation, and I am not ready for joint replacement; I wonder if maybe this is an invitation from You to move out here?"

Jack soon forgot all about the aches in his joints--in particular, his knees, which had been crushed in an auto accident when he was twenty-three. The MLK student union building was jammed with people from all faiths, and those who were spiritual, but not religious, who were imagining a new bottom line for America and her true place in the global village. Jack glided up the stairs to the second floor and deeply inhaled the energy emanating from over thirteen hundred American citizens who had gathered in the Pauley Ballroom in support of a new bottom line based on love, compassion, caring, ethical and ecological sensitivity, and behavior; and motivated by generosity, kindness, cooperation, nonviolence, and peace. Jack imagined a society that honored all human beings as embodiments of the sacred, a society that enhanced one's capacities to respond to the earth and the universe with awe, wonder, and radical amazement. He imagined the Kingdom of God, where men would turn their swords into plowshares and not make war anymore.

The invocation was offered by Father Louis Vitale, a Franciscan who reminded Jack of one of the least of the seven dwarves, until he spoke and revealed himself to be a man of profound wisdom, enrobed in well-worn burlap:

"The Holy One has called on us. In all of earth's sixty-five-million-year history, we are living in the most dangerous of times. The fact that a bomb was dropped on Hiroshima and two hundred thousand lives were vaporized within twenty minutes has not prevented man from dreaming up more ways to fill space with weapons of mass destruction. We were not created for militarism, but to turn our swords into plowshares. We have arrived here today by no accident. We have been summoned by the universe to claim the highest common ground. As the Dali Lama said, the radicalism of our age is to be compassionate human beings. We have been called to bring love and compassion back into the equation and assist others to connect with the deepest parts of themselves. Now is the time to realize, as never before, that when any of us suffer, we all suffer. All life is interconnected, interdependent, and greatly loved by the creator, the sustainer of the universe. We are called by love, for love, and to love."

Professor Nagler, M.C. and scholar, stoked the fire of hope within Jack. "We are not facing a spiritual crisis, but a spiritual opportunity. We offer the power of moral ideas to a country with a lot of religion yet which suffers from a great lack of spirituality and imagination. As William Blake said, 'Imagination is evidence of The Divine.' And spirituality is how we grow in sensitivity to ourselves, the other, and to God. Einstein wrote, 'Human beings are limited in time and space. We experience ourselves in an optical *delusion*. We see ourselves as separate from others. Our task must be to free ourselves from our prison of self. Only through compassion can we begin to embrace all of Creation.' The bumper sticker got it right; we are spiritual beings having a human experience."

George Lakoff, the author of *Don't Think of an Elephant*, affirmed what Jack already knew, that a nurturing parent raises a child as best they can to be responsible to self and others. A nurturing parent is not permissive or overindulgent, but models cooperation and honesty, and understands that everything is grace, an unconditional gift from God that one is free to accept or reject. Lakoff spoke about God as father, mother, all-knowing, all-good, all-powerful, and the source of the free gift of grace that will open one up to God in the world. Jack thought of Father Matthew Fox's recent publication, *A New Reformation.*

During Pentecost week, in 2005, Father Fox traveled to Wittenburg and *nailed* a new ninety-five theses to the church door, where Luther had nailed his five hundred years before. Father Fox wrote Jack's heart about an interfaith collaboration and community that intuits God as mother-father God of divine wisdom, and understands that the earth itself is to be tended; its health is just as much a moral imperative for us all as our human relationships. Jack had long ago rejected the concept of a punitive father God and understood that nature is God's primary temple, and war the greatest abomination.

Jack's mind wandered to the leper kisser, Francis of Assisi, and Jack thought, Frankie, you sang of sister moon and brother sun, and stood up to the dry rot and rigid religious sclerosis of the church in the twelfth century. I feel your presence here today in my bones, as much as in my soul. Jack went silent and in his mind, saw himself at nine with Father Tony, the diminutive ancient Spanish priest, who had held his hand all during his mother's funeral and chanted softly without ceasing, "Jesus called God Abba, and that means both daddy and mommy. So, God is both mommy and daddy, and now your mommy is a part of God. God is mommy and daddy: daddy and mommy divine."

Jack mused, "That and the daily readings are the best things I ever heard from the Roman Church." The heat from thirteen hundred bodies and the noonday sun made Jack fidgety, and even though his knees were aching most ferociously, he still craved a run, but as usual, was grateful for a fast walk. In seconds, he had escaped the crowd in Sproul Plaza and wandered around the rolling tree-canopied campus as endorphins flooded his blood; he no longer was aware of the crushing of bone on bone in his knees. He escaped in his mind to the good times before that Tuesday in September nearly four years ago, when his is wife, Julianne, had been vaporized in a stairwell in the Twin Towers.

At the first thought of that day when life all changed, Jack immediately roused himself back to reality, sat down, and again became aware of the aching in his knees. He pulled out the itinerary for the conference and thought, I need to figure out where I want to be these next few hours. I'd like to catch some of all these workshops and groups, but there are just too many choices. I'll start with "Environmental Policy," and then check out "Sacred Stewardship of the Earth," and maybe move onto "Theory and Practice of Nonviolence"--no, better yet, "Science and Spirit."

Jack absorbed what he could from each class, but could not sit still until 8 p.m. when Rev. Jim Wallis commanded his attention back in the Pauley Ballroom. "Religion's job is to pull out our best stuff; to help us be our best selves. Religion in America has been used and abused to control and manipulate millions of Christians.

"The good news is that there are millions more who are not represented by the Falwells and the Dobsons, and they are raising their voices and doing something about confronting the hijacking of the Bible to further political gain. All faith traditions battle with fundamentalism. Religion is meant to be a bridge, not a wedge.

"The seduction of the religious right by politicians is being challenged by our rapidly spreading grassroots sojourners community that stands up with a firm moral center and echoes Lincoln's refrain: what is needed today is reflection, penitence, humility, accountability, and that we should all seek to be on God's side.

"There are over three thousand verses in the Bible referring to the poor; this is the moral issue of our time. There are also the moral issues of poverty, ecology, and war; it is the church's job to address these moral issues, too. Separation of church and state does not mean the segregation of religion from the human dialogue....

"Our deepest choices are between hope and compassion. Hope is not a feeling or a state of mind, but an abiding choice you make because you have faith. Faith is supposed to change things that look impossible to be changed. Cynicism sees the world as it is and gives up trying to change it. Cynicism is a buffer against commitment....

"History testifies to the fact that all great changes came about by social justice movements that were based on faith and religious values. America has a proud history of progressive spiritual activism. We are the ones we have been waiting for. We can change the nation when we change the wind, and people of faith are called to be wind changers."

Wallis took a deep breath before continuing. "Let me explain exactly what an evangelical Christian is to be about. My evangelical roots are connected to the path laid down by evangelicals from the 19th century. They were the first to speak out against slavery and were the first supporters of female suffrage. In fact, the original altar call was the call to stand up against slavery...In this century, we are faced with nuclear weapons and the fact that the arms race put the world in grave danger. The world went to sleep, and now we have escalating proliferation, nations, and groups of angry people with nuclear warheads. The real security threat is coming from the gathering terrorists who are acquiring unsecured materials." Jim Wallis took another deep breath and ended with "Activists must be contemplatives, and contemplatives must act. The time has come for the Christian Right to meet the right Christians."

After a standing ovation for Wallis, the radiant Rabbi Lerner approached the lectern and beamed like a lighthouse turned on, and between his smile, said, "This is a historic event. Over thirteen hundred of you are here now, and we had to turn people away because we ran out of room. There is a hunger in America for deep spiritual truth, and the wisdom of the ages is again being spoken and heard. The time has come for the new bottom line. The new bottom line in society challenges the dominant ethos of materialism and selfishness and replaces it with institutions based not just on productivity, but also cooperation, mutuality, love, caring, ethical and ecological sensitivity, and awe and wonder at the grandeur of creation. We spiritual progressives challenge the misuse of God and religion by the Religious Right, just as we challenge those liberals and progressives who have been unsympathetic, even hostile, to spiritual and religious people.

"We of many faiths, and the spiritual but not religious, are calling for social justice and political freedom in the context of new structures of work, in caring communities and democratic social and economic arrangements. We of many faiths and those who are spiritual but not religious are inspired by compassion, generosity, nonviolence, and recognition of the spiritual dimension of life. We agree we desire a society that promotes love and generosity, recognizes the unity of all being, and understands our interdependence with all other people on the planet. We honor, with awe, wonder, and care, all of creation. We are extending the invitation to every church, synagogue, mosque, and ashram to affirm the prophetic vision of God as the champion of love, generosity, peace, social justice, and ecological sanity. We understand we are to give our highest attention to alleviating the suffering of the poor and powerless. We challenge the policies of governments and political parties that do not promote these values. The new bottom line replaces the old one based upon materialism and selfishness. The time has come; the time is now."

Jack reflected, "One reason the religious right is the only voice the mainstream media presents is that they have been the most vocal. The other problem is that the liberal and progressive media have only heard religion according to the right, so no wonder they tune religion out. I wonder how to get around it; how does a new voice rise out of the wilderness?"

The following day, Jack woke up still thinking about all he had experienced the day before. That Thursday morning, he heard Rick Ufford-Chase for the first time, and was blown away by how such a young man had accomplished so much. Rick was a founder of the Samaritans, co-moderator of the Presbyterian Peace Fellowship, a reservist for Christian Peacemakers Teams, and moderator of the 216th General Assembly of the Presbyterian Church.

Rick began with Isaiah 58: "'Shout it out, do not hold back. Raise your voice like a trumpet. Declare to my people...loosen the chains of injustice and set the oppressed free...share your food with the hungry and provide the poor wanderer with shelter--when you see the naked, clothe them...and if you spend yourselves in behalf of the hungry and satisfy the needs of the oppressed, your light will rise in the darkness and your night will become like the noonday sun.'"

Then Rick offered 1 John 4: "'Love comes from God and everyone who loves has been born of God and knows God, because God is love...There is no fear in love. For perfect love drives out fear...and those who love God love all their brothers and sisters.'"

Rick then spoke of his experiences on the Mexican border and the sanctity of all life. "We become holy in community; we must study and do Torah, and we build the Church by building community. God is within everyone, and the direct experience of working with, for, and among the poor and oppressed is the quickest way one can experience the presence of God."

After a few more speakers, Jack was overfilled and restless to move about. He wandered the campus while listening to a CD by Dave Rovics, one of the musicians at the conference. For the rest of the day, Jack couldn't get "They're Building a Wall" out of his head:

> They're building a wall,
> A wall between friends,
> A wall that justifies any means to their ends
> Many feet thick and twenty feet high
> They're building the wall between water and land,
> So we can eat fruit and they can eat sand
> A wall to keep quiet that which you fear most
> They're building the wall
> To remove reality from your facts on the ground,
> A wall to keep distant the terrible sound
> Of the houses that crumble and the children that die,
> A wall to keep separate the truth from the lie
> A wall made of brick but bricks can be broken
> When the people of Zion have finally awoken
> And said no more walls, no more refugees,
> No more keeping people upon their knees
> And before apartheid was ended they were building a wall.

That evening, Bishop John Shelby Spong began by asking, "What has happened to Christianity? I have been a student of the Bible my entire life. I am a committed Christian and open to anyone's opinion, but not to their own facts. The Bible has been used to justify slavery, segregation, to deny woman equality, and to promote war. A lot of evil happens when the Bible is misunderstood and misused. In the name of God, men have become murderers. We live in a world where people in power get to define those without power. The prophets spoke the word of God in concrete circumstances and throughout history. Hosea spoke of God as love. Amos understood that worship and justice go together. Micah confronted Israel with their behavior, and God again told the people what is required: 'Do justice, love mercy, and walk humbly with your Lord.'"

On Friday morning, in Newman Hall, in the sanctuary known as Holy Spirit Catholic Church, Betsy Rose led the crowd in singing,

> *There's a new world coming,*
> *There's a new world coming,*
> *There's a new world coming,*
> *I can hear her breathing.*

Jack marveled at all the smiling faces around him and about the fact that he had not been in a Catholic church since his youngest sister was wed twenty-four years ago by their brother, Father Mike.

Rev. Dr. Welton Gaddy, leader of the Interfaith Alliance Foundation and pastor at Northminster Baptist Church in L.A, brought the crowd to their feet from the start. "We are people hungry to get on with the business we are about. American politics have already been transformed by religion and spirit, just not the one we believe and desire. We are a deeply divided nation, and the substance of what passes for religion looks like the stuff of politics. There is no such thing as the American religion, for we are a country of over seventy-five faith traditions. The proper role of religion is to link core values, to cooperate, to respect all people, to promote peace, justice, and compassion, and to protect the weak, poor, and the environment. Today, politics have become a form of religion. We need freedom for and from that kind of religion. Religion should command, inspire hope, and build bridges between other faiths and to those with no faith at all. We will be restless until we speak the truth to power. We will be restless until we comfort the afflicted and disturb the comfortable. We will be restless until we become a nation that cares for its entire people and lives with respect towards all others in the global village. May we all be restless, and then speak and act in peace and goodwill, in the spirit of cooperation."

Jack's mind wandered back to what he had read in *Subversive Orthodoxy: Outlaws, Revolutionaries, and Other Christians in Disguise*, as soon as he noted the author Robert Inchausti was on the morning's program. Inchausti had written, "To change the world we must become receptacles of God's love, understanding and goodwill. We must have faith, not merely of the mind, but of the heart that surrenders the whole man to the divine inflow...moral action links personal salvation directly to social responsibility...Victory is not the goal, doing God's will is."

Jack reflected everyday on what God wanted from him, and spent most of the time in the dark. He left his ruminating behind when Robert Inchausti stood at the podium and proclaimed, "This country was built by spiritual progressives. Spiritual progressives are the center and we are not a mushy middle. The new bottom line is not new at all; it was already articulated by the Puritans. The Puritans were about charity, not power, and that is the true American tradition. We radical spiritual activists are the heart of the American tradition. Of course we know there will always be the poor among us, but our call always has been to respond."

At the break, Jack was the first one out of Newman Hall, and he strode directly to UC Botanical Garden to be with over three thousand California-native plants and sublime silence. On his way back for the afternoon session, he met a rabbi from Australia and a pastor from England, who had traveled to America specifically to attend the conference. Jack marveled at the possibilities of what might happen on the other side of the world when these men shared what they had experienced.

Jack parted ways with them and headed back to Newman Hall to hear Father Fox speak about the New Reformation. And Jack thought, Everyday, I am crossing paths with so many incredible people. Last month I sat in Reverend Ateek's Sabeel office in Jerusalem, and the other night I sat next to Abla, his sister-in-law, at a meeting of MEPAC. There, I met a community of tireless workers in the political realm keeping the issue of peace and justice in Israel and Palestine on the front burner. The next day, I was in the office of this riot of a woman who founded MECA--funny, crusty, and salty, with a most compassionate heart. For seventeen years, MECA has been bearing witness to the West Bank and Gaza. Then there's Doug, the guy from that last work group; I have never known anyone like him. Talk about connecting with one's feminine side! It has got to be holy wisdom, the feminine divinity that led him to photograph the neighborhood gardens in his town and display them on Main Street, to bring the folks around and build community. Then he takes up dancing and singing--his wife must be wondering who she is now sleeping with.

It was apparent to Jack when he returned to Newman Hall that the fire department's maximum allowed crowd size was being ignored. In the center of the sanctuary of Holy Spirit Catholic Church, Father Fox proclaimed, "Forget original sin; remember original blessing. There are two Christianities in our midst. One worships a punitive father and seeks obedience at all costs. It is patriarchal, demonizes woman, the earth, science, gays, lesbians, and deep thought. It builds on fear and it supports empire-builders. Its theology includes a punitive father in the sky and teaches original sin. The other Christianity recognizes the original blessing that all beings derive from. We recognize awe, not sin, not guilt, as the starting point of true religion. We recognize a divinity who is source of all things and is as much mother as father, as much female as male. We honor creation and diversity. When God created everything, He pronounced it all good. We are here to make love to life. Yes, we are here to make love to life. Delight in creation and take your dreams into our politics and institutions. We live in the midst of a suicidal economy, motivated by love of money. We have reached a dead end. What we need to turn it around are hearts in love with life. How do we do it? We first must move from domination to partnership, and we begin by educating our young in awe and wonder, not how to take tests. Awe leads to reverence, which leads to gratitude, which will reinvent our species. This is the task of our generation: to regain awe. The three Rs need to be balanced by the ten Cs: contemplation, creativity, chaos, compassion, courage, critical consciousness, community, celebration, ceremony, and character.

"In community, people remain united, despite everything that divides them. In capitalist society, people are isolated, separated, despite everything that should hold them together. We are in the midst of an epic struggle between community and capitalistic society. We need a new narrative. It is the economy of materialism; it is the virus of affluenza that has weakened family life."

CHAPTER 13:

CATS AND COMPASSION

TERESE ABSENTMINDEDLY CARESSED THE pristine one hundred sheet Official Mead Composition notebook during breakfast. Terese had been writing poetry for years, but refused to let anyone read any of it. She even refused Jake and had a secret ritual. The first full moon after she completed a book, she would light a fire at 1 a.m. in the fire pit where Jake barbequed. She would read her words one last time by the light of the moon, then toss in the Official Mead Composition notebook. She would walk in circles as it burned, and only after the embers died did her ritual circular walk.

After breakfast, she brushed her teeth, grabbed her backpack, and set off into the woods, pondering, "I have been wrestling with this idea for a book for too long. Will this try end up in the fire, too? As always, I do not know; I never know anything before I begin, and as long as I stay open to learn as I go, it will be okay, okay. Christ have mercy on me and help me, please! How do I explain concrete walls to little children, and why men choose violence? How do you explain irrational adult behavior to little ones? Why do men choose hatred, injury, discord, error, and darkness to love, pardon, unity, truth, and light? Why is that? Christ have mercy on us all!"

Terese sighed deeply and immediately became aware as the sun's rays filtered through the thickly canopied trail, and sensed the scurrying of small creatures around her, who were camouflaged beneath the thick carpet of leaves she tread upon. At the end of the trail, a gazebo had been erected in memory of a fallen soldier in a long ago war. Terese blessed herself as she entered, then opened her backpack, removed three gel pens and the one hundred sheet Official Mead Composition notebook, and groaned, "Okay, okay."

Terese stared at the upper left corner of the virgin leaf of paper in her Official Mead Composition notebook and sighed as she chewed the end of a gel pen. After a few deep breathes, she set the tip down at the uppermost intersection of the red vertical line and the first of twenty-four horizontal blue lines, and watched in amazement as words filled the page:

> I am an old crone now, but I once was your age.
> I remember, when I was seven years old, I saw a picture in the newspaper of a little naked girl running in terror from a mushroom cloud, and I wondered, why did that girl have to run for her life in her hometown, when in mine, everyone was safe and happy?
> That girl in the picture wasn't safe, and she was not happy. I wondered about her, and me, and my hometown, and America.
> I am an old crone now and I still wonder...
> When images from Vietnam were on the TV screen, I was a mom of three and seven months pregnant with twins. I went into early labor on that day; a shot rang out in my hometown, and America's prophet bled on the concrete of Memphis.

Terese sighed, flipped to a clean page, and wondered, "I am getting nowhere. I want to explain why there is war to children, but I don't know how to go about it."

She chewed the end of her gel pen and stared into the pistil and stamen of a white and violet day lily that grew next to the gazebo. A gunfire round of riveting from the redheaded woodpecker above her head brought Terese back to her empty page, and she sighed, "Christ, have mercy on me. What's the deal with me? How could I think I could write a story to explain war to children, when I don't understand why war has to be?"

She bit her lip and sighed a few more times, before putting the gel pen back to the paper. She lit up like a Christmas tree as the words flew from her fingers:

> Have you heard the one about Dorothy and her cats?

Dorothy was about your age when her tiny orange and calico cat named Peachez met with an early demise. You see, little Peachez, barely a year old, got too big for her breeches, and snuck out Dorothy's front door. Nobody knew except Rikki, the deer dog who lived next door.

Rikki could not resist his nature to hunt, and Peachez was most exotic fare, for in this neighborhood, cats lived inside. Little defenseless Peachez never had a chance, for Rikki bit right through the neck of that tiny orange and calico cat.

Oh, how Dorothy mourned; oh, how she grieved; after a week, her mother could take it no more, and told her, 'Girl, you need a new kitty!'

Dorothy agreed.

'Then, I will call the cat league and see what they have in stock, okay, Dorothy?'

'Okay, okay, do it for me, please.'

'Happily,' her mom told her, as she dialed the animal league.

Dorothy could not believe it when she heard her mother say, 'Hi, have you got any kitties that need a home?'

Dorothy exploded. 'No, not just any kitty, I know exactly what I want. I want a pure white cat with blue eyes the color of the summer sky, and I'll call him Bob.'

'Okay, okay. Did you hear all that, lady from the animal league?'

'Yes, I did, and, ah--good luck with it. I have a lot of cats that could be Bob; some have pure white fur, but not a one has blue eyes.'

'Okay, thanks, we will continue on,' Dorothy's mom sighed, as she hung up the phone. 'Girl, I have to pick up the dry cleaning next to the veterinarian's office. Come with me now, and maybe someone there will be able to help you find your Bob with blue eyes and white fur on.'

For the first time since Peachez demise, Dorothy smiled when she said, 'Okay, okay.'

Dorothy and her mom stood in line at the vet's office for an interminable time before a doe-eyed brunette, as thin as a French-cut string bean, noticed them and said, 'Hi, can I help you?'

Dorothy exploded. 'I am looking for the cat of my dreams; he has pure white fur and eyes the color of the summer sky, and his name is Bob.'

'Well, this is most numinous. You see, I have a five-year-old cat back in storage that needs a home. He is very sad, for he has been in a cage for almost seven months. He has licked off all his hair, and he pouts a lot.

'You see, it was Thanksgiving week when his first family dropped him off. They didn't love him. They tossed him away. They wanted the doctor to give him a shot, to put him to sleep. But I said, "No way! I'll put that cat in storage, and one day, someone will come in here and take him away."'

Dorothy's mom interrupted. 'There must be a reason that family tossed that cat away.'

The doe-eyed string bean replied, 'Sister, let me tell you, this cat is no more neurotic than any other cat I have known. I will not lie to you, for he is indeed one neurotic cat, who never was a beauty. But he did have white fur when he came in here, and his eyes are still as blue as a summer sky. He is most definitely OC; he licks himself a lot, and so, is now as bald as a bat.

'Oh, by the way, he whines like a banshee and paces about. You see, after his upsetting Thanksgiving holiday, the vet fixed him for Christmas, and no doubt you can imagine why he is naturally still quite upset about that. Oh, by the way, he has claws, and since he is too old for surgery, they must stay. But, sister, I assure you, he's no more or less neurotic than any other cat around. Follow me into the back room, and you will see that he really is a cool cat; you should take him away.'

'I think Dorothy wants a blue-eyed baby kitty, not one so worn-out,' Dorothy's mother pleaded, looking hopefully at her daughter.

'I don't care how old he is, as long as he is my Bob,' Dorothy shouted over the cacophony of barking and yelping, as the doe-eyed string bean stopped in front of the center cage and announced, 'Surely, I told you--this cat has always been called Bob.'

And with that, she turned, and with one smooth motion, unlatched the cage and pulled out a long scrawny cat, with a few patches of white fur, but mostly skin showing. His enormous blue eyes, the color of the summer sky, looked into Dorothy's, and he moaned like a baby in pain; Dorothy proclaimed, 'He's the one!'

Dorothy took him home on her shoulder as her mom drove the Focus, and Bob never moved a muscle, nor made a sound. Dorothy's mom thought, This won't be so bad, right?

As soon as Dorothy put Bob down in her room, he wailed and moaned, and Dorothy did not know what to do, until her mom told her, 'He's just like a baby, and you may have to walk the floors holding him all night. Welcome to motherhood.'

Dorothy gleefully picked Bob back up and carried him around on her shoulder, just like you would a little baby. Every single time she put Bob down, he would whine, kvetch, and pace all around, and would stare at her with his blue eyes the color of a summer sky. Dorothy swore she heard him say, 'Sister, I've got the blues bad, and I can't calm down unless you carry me around.'

The very next night, the bombs hit Baghdad. All night, Dorothy walked the floors with Bob, the blue-eyed cat on her shoulder, and a heart breaking, breaking, breaking for all the innocents caught up in the crossfire. She knew she was connected. You are, too.

In the 11th century, Hildegard of Bingen saw: 'God responds speedily whenever the blood of innocence is being shed. Of this the angel choirs are singing and re-echoing their praise. And yet at the loss of innocence clouds are weeping.'

Bob, the blue eyed cat, has now calmed down. He doesn't want to be held, and he never makes a sound. His hair has grown back, pure white and coarse as grit. Into his summer sky blue eyes, clouds of cataracts have moved. He moves slowly, slowly, slowly. Bob tucks his front legs under his chest and gently bows as he gets down. What a contemplative Bob is, for deliberate movement is prayer.

A new kitty has moved into Dorothy's house, too. A black and white long–haired, green-eyed feline named Oreo. Dorothy found her when she was only a week old and abandoned by her cat mom, who left the litter and never returned. Dorothy fed the baby kitty every three hours for three weeks with an eyedropper, and kept her warm.

Oreo has now grown big and strong, and likes to play, but sometimes can be a pain. Bob always treats her gently, even when she bites his tail; he either plays or he walks away.

Terese stretched and moaned, "That's as far as I can go today."

Chapter 14:

9/11/05 and the Gulfport Blues

For the past twenty-two years of Sunday mornings, Dr. Jake Hunter had navigated the tannic colored waters of the Withlacoochee River in the dark, so as to arrive at the center of Lake Silver just before first light. For miles, the eastern vista manifested multitudes of eighty-feet-tall and six-hundred-year-old cypress trees. The rising sun that backlit the cypress always filled Jake with awe, but this morning, his mood was most foul. He had been consumed with rage from the instant he viewed the first images from New Orleans the week before, and deep pain had wounded America's soul. Jake spit out of the side of the boat and cursed local, state, and federal bureaucracy for failing the least and most vulnerable.

"I am so pissed! What Hurricane Katrina blew in and exposed was that the empire has no clothes! What happened in the Big Easy was foretold three years ago in a five-part series in the New Orleans *Times-Picayune*. Then, last October's *National Geographic* fictional story became fact, as it had laid out the scene in incredible detail, which became reality on TV. Christ, have mercy! Local officials and FEMA knew about the probability that even a slow-moving category three hurricane would cause catastrophic loss and a lot of human misery. Those 19th-century levees were not designed for that eventuality! Now, maybe we all will wake up to the facts, that in the third millennium, all our infrastructures need a physician, stat! The very innards of our nation are collapsing, and a government that has been commissioned to protect its citizens blew it, big time! I am so pissed that a billion tax dollars a day go to support a war in Iraq, and not one level of government would bother to scrounge up the bucks for adequate supplies of food, water, and medicine. I am so pissed!"

Jake rubbed his burning arms while cursing the spinal cord impingement that caused it, and then moaned, "Christ, have mercy on us for ignoring our sentinels! For years, climatologists have predicted and warned us that powerful storms will occur more frequently in this century, because of the rising sea level from global warming. The hardest-working marsh in America is the Louisiana bayou, and we have neglected its health. For three hundred years, men have built walls and levees to control that mighty force of nature, and it has 'wrecked' havoc on New Orleans's natural defenses. From the Mississippi border to the Texas state line, Louisiana is losing its protective fringe of marshes and barrier islands faster than any place in the U.S."

Jake hushed as first light broke, and he sat, motionless and awed by the view, until a mosquito bit his cheek; he again cursed, spat, and then growled into the wind, "That's the other thing that's pissing me off. People have been propagandized to buy cypress mulch, and that has led to logging companies raping the areas where ivory-bill woodpeckers once roamed. Florida and Louisiana are being violated by timber companies buying up private property, so that they can cut down these magnificent trees that are part of the filtering system for wetland health. If people would only wake up and use leaves, pine bark, or pine straw, which are much cheaper and work just as well, we could put a stop to this particular raping of Mother Earth. It's time to stop cutting down our cypress trees, and Homeland Security money should go to restoring the homeland."

Back at the A-frame, Terese sipped from her steaming mug of black brew and checked her email, to find report 57 from Jerry Levin, a reporter and full-time volunteer with Christian Peacemaker Teams (CPT). She sighed repeatedly as she read about the start of a new school year in Hebron, for it wasn't good. She had spent a few hours in Hebron in June, and had not forgotten it for one day since.

"Christ, have mercy! These teachers and kids trying to get to school are threatened and hassled by these erratic and illegal settlers, and a trigger-happy IDF! What a daily life to have to contend with! I cannot imagine watching my child have to go through a checkpoint or be verbally and physically abused just to get to school! What are we teaching these kids, when they grow up looking up the barrel of an Israeli soldier's Uzi?"

Next, she opened a press conference summary of September 6, 2005, from Dr. Mustafa Bargouthi, regarding the aftermath of the "disengagement," and the bottom line was more settlers, more walls, and more corruption in the PA.

"This is all miserable news! The lawlessness in the Palestinian territories from political corruption is staggering! 'Ninety percent of security violations in Palestine are committed by security forces and intelligence. These forces must be disciplined; the rule of law and an independent judiciary must be installed. [And] it is estimated that 30 percent of the 160,000 salaried government employees do not attend work of any kind. This kind of corruption and nepotism must be ended.'" [Dr. M. Barghouthi, Palestinian National Initiative. September 6, 2005]

Terese moaned when she read about the violations since the ceasefire agreement of February 8. "Christ, have mercy! Seventy-five Palestinians, including seventeen innocent children, and fourteen Israelis, including two innocent children, have been murdered. Two thousand Palestinians have been arrested; there have been 2,306 checkpoints imposed, and 8,700 acres of Palestinian land has been confiscated by the Israeli government! And how can these settlers sleep at night, after attacking Palestinians 394 times since the ceasefire agreement? I feel bad about these screwed-up settlers, but they are a cult that has been allowed to get out of control. The Israeli government enticed and encouraged them to settle in illegal land, and this is what it has come to! And yet, the illegal settlements continue!

"And, what a farce the so-called disengagement in Gaza was. The Israeli government still controls all access to Gaza by land, sea, and air. 'Only 25 of over 150 settlements will be dismantled, and only 8,475 of over 436,000 settlers [less than 2 percent of settlers] have been evacuated. Meanwhile, in the past year, 12,800 new settlers have moved into the West Bank--50 percent more settlers than were evacuated.'[IBID]

"This is no withdrawal, this is BS! Until Palestinians have control of Gaza's borders and a guaranteed passage between Gaza and the West Bank, it is not a withdrawal; it's just BS propaganda! And Gaza is less than 6 percent of the occupied territories, and that leaves 94 percent of Palestinian territories under the boot of the IDF. The corruption in the PA government and hot tempers from those under occupation are a powder keg that's getting ready to blow! What's it going to take to wake the world up to the fact that most of our problems with radical Islamist fundamentalist militants leads us back to the conflict in Israel and Palestine? All roads do indeed lead to Jerusalem. What's it going to take before the International community gets it together and insists, in unity, upon the upholding of international law as the rule we all live by? And that includes Israel and America, too, for both ratified the Universal Declaration of Human Rights. I wonder, what's the point of signing on, but then not doing it?

"What's it going to take to wake up the legions of blind U.S. Christian Zionists to their indifference to the misery of their sisters and brothers in Israel and Palestine? Their blind allegiance to the Israeli government has allowed our best friend in the world to become a big bully. What's it going to take to break through the ignorance that hard-earned U.S. tax dollars are being used to continue the occupation and apartheid wall?"

Jack slammed the U-Haul's gate down as he told Maureen, "This is the fourth year since Julianne was vaporized on Floor 101 of the North Twin Tower, and it took that misery in the Delta to get me to finally part with her belongings and much more. If you would have told me two weeks ago that I would be driving a filled-to-the-max twenty-four-foot U-Haul down to refugees in Mississippi on the anniversary date of Julianne's demise, I would not have been able to even imagine it. But, if I don't do something to help somehow, I will go nuts, or I will fall off the wagon one more time.

"Here we are, two weeks later, and many Gulfport residents still have not seen FEMA! I hope and pray that this misery in the Delta will wake up America to the fact that abject poverty surrounds our cocoons of consumerism and self-absorbed lives. We all need to do something to help those among us who had so little and now have nothing at all.

"Mo! I know what we can do; we can build Habitat for Humanity housing within the gates of South Hampton and Beverly Hills--you know, resettle the refugees equitably, let every state take some in--and let's build them housing in the best school districts! That could very well break the poverty cycle; what do you think, Mo?"

Maureen smirked to fight back tears as she hugged Jack and spoke. "Brother, I know you are nuts! But, in "Over the Teacups," Oliver Wendell Holmes, Jr., wrote: 'There never was an idea stated that woke men out of their stupid indifference but its originator was spoken of as a crank.' So, Jack, your kind of nuts is good. Out of a town of seventeen thousand, only you thought to contact all the churches around and announce you would drive down donations of food, water, and toiletries to help American refugees on the anniversary of your own misery."

"Watching those images and being powerless to help was excruciating. It also forced me to finally part with some things I needed to let go. Mo, not much matters when one's heart is broken and soul has been torn, but I have learned that I must do something, or else..."

CHAPTER 15:

A CONFRONTATIONAL CONVERSATION

"FATHER PAUL, YOU CANNOT possibly be telling me that an Episcopal priest has been taken in by fundamentalist theology?" Terese incredulously asked the new assistant to the rector at St. Mary's Episcopal Church in Orlando, who also served at the noon mass every Wednesday.

Father Paul Hendricks was a passionate evangelist on a mission to convert every Jew he encountered to become a Christian. Terese had kept her silence for the first six months she had been listening to his Wednesday noon sermons, but finally broke her silence after the rest of the parishioners had departed.

Paul sighed and shook his head. "Look, Mrs. Hunter, I read your op/ed in the newspaper about Israel and Palestine, and we both agree we want peace; we just go about it differently."

"Father, let me say that the fastest growing cult in the U.S.A. is the cult of Christian Zionism. Approximately 25 million U.S. Christians believe as you do, and I am most depressed to see that the simple answers of fundamentalism have reached their tentacles into the thinking man's church. You just preached for thirteen minutes on Genesis 12:3--'I will bless those who bless you, and the one who curses you I will curse: and in you all the families of the world are blessed'--as if God meant blessings to be political power and military might. Father, surely you understand that the belief of the ancient Israelites, who held that they were chosen, as if they were somehow special from others, as if God esteemed them above others, is just basic primitive nationalism. Come on,

Father, looking down on one's enemies to foster one's own tribal interest and praying to God to smite one's enemies is what the ancients did. Isn't it about time we moved beyond that limited thinking?"

Father Paul clenched his fists and held them behind his back, as he suppressed a simmering rage. He stood nine inches above Terese's upturned head, and with a slick smile and condescending tone told her, "Mrs. Hunter, you are very misled. The text is understood to mean a blessing to Abraham's lineage--"

Terese cut in. "Agreed! And Genesis 12:3 was promised even before Ishmael, the father of the Arab nation, and Isaac, the Jew, were born! And what about the very first mention of Israel? Jacob was renamed Israel for having wrestled and struggled with God. That is how I understand Israel; everyone who struggles and wrestles with God is Israel, too. Israel means more than a geographical location, Father Paul."

"Mrs. Hunter, the modern state of Israel is the fulfillment of the prophetic scriptures, and God's covenant with Israel is eternal, exclusive, and will not be abrogated. I refer you to Genesis 12:1-7, 15:4-7, 17:1-8; Leviticus 26:44-45; and Deuteronomy 7:7.8."

"And Father, I refer you to Matthew 5:43-45, which does not only critique Genesis 12:3; it blows it apart, for Christ commanded, 'Love your enemies, bless them that curse you, do good to them that hate you, and pray for them that despitefully use you, that you maybe children of your Father.'"

The two had reached Paul's SUV and he silently prayed he could make a swift escape, but Terese had positioned herself at the driver's door, and if he were to open it swiftly, she could be easily moved aside. Father Paul entertained the thought for more than a moment, but remained mute and still, as the tiny woman exploded with a torrent of words.

"Look, blind allegiance to the Israeli government has allowed them to become a big bully, and isn't God always on the side of the oppressed? My sense is that you Zionists see the political state of Israel as a replacement for Christ, at the center of the Christian faith, and that certainly is not Christianity. How do you take Genesis 12:3 to literally mean that blessings equal land and political power, yet ignore God's promise in Genesis 21:17-20 to 'make a great nation out of Ishmael's descendents' and that 'God was with the boy.' Yet your way of thinking allows the growing apartheid wall to continue, and supports occupation and oppression of people that God also made promises to."

"Mrs. Hunter, why don't you make an appointment and we can discuss this further? I really have to go."

"Okay, I can take a hint, but let me leave you with this: when religion and politics are in bed together, everybody gets screwed! The Israeli government is using you Zionists as apologists in support of their agenda of illegal occupation and settlements in the West bank, Golan, and Gaza, on literal biblical grounds taken out of context. Your blind allegiance to every act of Israel, understood as being orchestrated by God and which should therefore be condoned, supported, and even praised, makes me want to puke! And I wonder about the true motives of Christians who actually relish the idea of Armageddon and love to speculate on who gets 'left behind.' Christ was very clear that there will be a lot of wailing and gnashing of teeth by those who were so sure they were in, but get left out. God has always been on the side of the oppressed, and your uncritical endorsement and justification for Israel's racist and apartheid policies are an abomination."

The stunned and silent priest watched in relief as Terese turned, flipped her braid, and walked away.

CHAPTER 16:

ALL I'VE GOT

JAKE GROANED, "AHHHH--TERESE, I cannot believe, after all these years, you are finally allowing me the opportunity to hear the words you spend hours pouring into those Mead Composition books you buy by the case. How many years has it been going on that you write your heart into those books, then toss them in the lit barbeque pit in your wannabe Druidess ritual when the full moon calls to you? I have never been bored by you, but you are getting a little too strange and most outspoken. You have skated the edge for years, my dear, and now I think you have skated through the veil one too many times. What has gotten into you that you just cannot shut up about things you never spoke aloud about in your life? I think you should reconsider offering that last poem at the church talent show; they will burn you at the stake."

"Look, for years, I was the proper Episcopalian wife and mother, did all the little things I saw to do, and kept my mouth shut about all the injustice and hypocrisy around. But I wrote it all down in my Official Mead Composition Notebook for all these years, and because a proper Episcopalian wife and mother does not say, much less think such things as I wrote down, I had to burn them; they were too inflammatory! But ever since I switched to Top Flight Composition books out of Chattanooga, Tennessee, something has come over me. I must now give voice to the words that spill out of me; I must break silence."

"But do you see the road ahead of you? Have you considered the cost? You have always been impulsive, but you went about it in a quiet, unobtrusive, and little way; you never caused a stir. Something's changed, and I think I want you to have a brain scan--you know, make sure you don't have a lesion that is making you wackier than you have ever been before. If you check out okay, then there has got to be another reason why an old woman who has the easiest life around wants to agitate the status quo. I wonder what you are getting out of it, Terese. What motivates you, old woman?"

Terese sighed, then looked directly into Jake's cerulean eyes and softly spoke. "Let me play you another poem, for I think it will answer your concerns."

She picked up her red guitar, then strummed the chords to "All Along the Watchtower" and began to sing, just a breath above a whisper:

> *All I've got is a red guitar, three chords, and the truth.*
> *All I've got is my bleedin' heart, and a voice cryin' out*
> *of the wilderness to you*
> *I see there is a way out of here,*
> *a way to get some relief*
> *Listen to me, all you little ones; come in here:*
> *Listen to me;*
> *I am very small, I am so very, very small,*
> *So small as to indwell the heart of every atom,*
> *and I am beyond your comprehension...*
> *Listen to me;*
> *I hear wisdom calling from the highest point of the city;*
>
> **'Wisdom has built her house and She calls to all; 'Come, eat my*
> *food and drink my wine and you will live abundant life and*
> *walk in the ways of understanding.' [*Proverbs 9: 4-6]*
>
> *Wisdom calls; I have built it; will you come? Do you have eyes to*
> *see and ears to hear?'*
>
> *Holy Wisdom: The Feminine Divinity: Hokema,*
>
> *Who was with The Word from the beginning,*
>
> *She is One with Him and He with Her;*
>
> *Pure Being; One God;*

One Creator; One Lover of All the Human Family...

Brother, I see you lookin' at me like you think I've skated off the edge and maybe I have, so, what's it to you?

Let me tell a little story to illuminate you,

if you haven't heard

The one about the Rabbi Hillel,

Who lived 100 years before The Christ walked the earth

Let me tell you,

That wise Rabbi understood that the Hebrew Hokema; Holy Wisdom; The Feminine Divinity

Was the same as the Greek understanding of The Logos: The Word: The Way

It was Saints Paul and John who first understood

The Word was good and

The Word was The Logos

The Logos is The Christ.

It was Lennon on Rubber Soul who told:

"The Word is just The Way."

Little children, listen to me and use your imagination,

And you will see that before Christ walked the earth a man,

He was already a She: Hokema, Holy Wisdom; the Feminine Divinity

Isn't that good news?

The God Head is One Pure Being;

As much male as female

As much mommy as daddy.

And we are all children of Her Universe;

And **He is the oldest personality because He is the origin of everything;

And everything is born of Him.

He is the supreme controller of the universe,

The maintainer and instructor of humanity.

He is smaller than the smallest.

He indwells the heart of every atom and

She is beyond the Universe.

Wisdom is calling,

She is rattling your windows and shaking your walls

With some more good news of the

Three witnesses,

And three always beats one

And not just that,

I've got a fourth!

Get out your Good Book, sisters and brothers, and chew on this:

Matthew 12:31-32, Mark 3:28-29, and Luke 12:10

Are simpatico with heretical Thomas saying 44:

Jesus said: "Whoever blasphemes against the father will be forgiven, whoever blasphemes against the son will be forgiven, but whoever blasphemes against the Holy Spirit will not be forgiven either on earth or in heaven."

Listen to me, what Christ is saying, is that God is within every sister, brother, and all Creation,

Wake up to your own divinity and

Get a clue, Christian:

His ways are not your ways and Her thoughts are not your thoughts

Dominion never meant to rape and plunder,

But to nurture, care and love

And if you have not love, you have nothing at all

And on that final day we all will stand naked before The Creator

And we have been warned that there will be a lot of wailing and gnashing of teeth

By those who were so sure they were in, because they will be the ones left out.

Christian, hear the wind begin to howl."

Jake moaned, "You sound like a prophet, and you know what happened to the prophets, right?"

Terese laughed. "Jake, remember John Belushi as Jake Blues in the good Blues Brothers movie? Remember when he kept saying, 'I am on a mission from God?' That is exactly how I feel; I am on a mission to shake up the annual church talent show this year. With a Bishop who can't get over the fact that there is an HONEST gay bishop, and my priest ignores the exodus of our sisters and brothers in Christ in the Holy Land, I am doing something more than making coffee and clearing the tables; I am going to do my little poem, and what do you think will happen, Jake?"

"I think you will get stoned."

"Jake, I don't care the least what anyone thinks of me, as long as they do some thinking! It is their apathy and passivity that I am confronting. Their lukewarm-ness makes me want to puke! I have no patience any longer with comfortable Christians; they need to be agitated into deep thinking and doing The Beatitudes. Christ promised that the peacemakers are the children of God, and he said, 'I came that you would have life to the full; abundant life.' And that takes thinking deep and then taking action."

"You may be halfway to being a saint, Terese, for I am convinced that there are really only two sins: selfishness and being boring, and you certainly are not that.

Attwater, Donald. *The Practice of the Presence of God.* Springfield, Illinois: Templegate Publishers, 1974.

Azar-Rucquoi, Adele. "Fundamentally, It's Love." *Faith in Focus*, April 29, 2002. http://www.authorsden.com/visit/view/article.asp?AuthorID=21384&id=14062.

The Columbia Encyclopedia. Fifth Edition. Columbia University Press, 1993, s.v. "Vatican Council, Second."

Dylan, Bob. *Shot of Love.* Columbia Records, Inc. 1981.
Ehrman, Bart D. *Lost Christianities.* New York: Oxford University Press, 2003.

Einstein, Albert. *Out of My Later Years.* New York: Random House Wings Books, 1956.

Foster, Richard J. *Streams of Living Water.* New York: Harper Collins Publishers, 1998.

Fox, Matthew. A New Reformation. www.WisdomUniversity.org

Inchausti, Robert. "Subversive Orthodoxy: Outlaws, Revolutionaries and other Christians in Disguise." www.brazospress.com

King, Martin Luther, Jr. *A Testament of Hope: The Essential Writings and Speeches of Martin Luther King.* New York: HarperSanFrancisco, 1990.

Lerner, Rabbi Michael. *Healing Israel/Palestine.* Berkeley: Tikkun Books, 2003.

Levin, Jerry. *West Bank Diaries.* HOPE Publishing House: www.hope-pub.com, 2005.

Levin, Jerry. *Reflections of My First Noel.* www.hope-pub.com 1999

Lewisy, John. "Martin Luther King Jr.'s Special Bond with Israel." *San Francisco Chronicle*, January 21, 2002. http://www.likud.nl/ref27.html.

Meyer, Marvin. *The Gospel of Thomas*. New York: Harper Collins Publishers, 1992.

Newell, Philip J. *The Book of Creation*. New Jersey: Paulist Press, 1999.

Peck, Scott M. *The Different Drum-Community Making and Peace*. New York: Simon and Shuster, Inc., 1987.

"Quotes and Ideas: Independence." Hearts and Minds: Information for Change. http://www.heartsandminds.org/quotes/Independence.htm.

Scaruffi, Piero. "A Timeline of the Middle-East." http://www.scaruffi.com/politics/middleea.html.

Smith, Houston. *The World's Religions*. New York: Harper Collins Publishers, 1991.

Strindberg, Anders. "Forgotten Christians." *The American Conservative*, May 24, 2004. http://www.amconmag.com/2004_05_24/article.html.

"Timeline 1967-1968." HistoryCentral.com. http://www.multied.com/dates/1967.html.

Washington, James M., Ed. *A Testament of Hope: The Essential Writings and Speeches of Martin Luther King Jr.* New York: Harper Collins Publishers, 1986.

Wheatley, Margaret. "Paying Attention to What's Tapping Us on the Shoulder." Women's World Institute Web site. http://www.womensworldinstitute.com/wheatley.html.

The World On-Line. "A Middle East History" Part 2. http://www.theworld.org/archive/mideast/05212002.htm (accessed May 29, 2004).

The Yom Kippur War. http://www.historylearningsite.co.uk/yom_kippur_war_of1973.htm. (accessed June 6, 2004).

END NOTES

[1] Meyer, *Gospel of Thomas*, 23.

[2] Ibid.

[3] Ibid.

[4] Ibid., 41.

[5] Azar-Rucquoi, Fundamentally, 19.

[6] King, *Testament*, 217-218.

[7] Lewisy, *San Francisco Chronicle*, Jan. 21, 2002.

[8] King, *Testament*, 219.

[9] Micah 6:8.

[10] King, *Testament*, 241.

[11] Peck, *Different Drum*, 186-208.

[12] *Columbia Encyclopedia*, 5th edition, s.v. "Vatican Council, Second."

[13] Einstein, *Later Years*, 268.

[14] Meyer, *Gospel*, 43.

[15] Pastor John R. Mabry, Berkeley, email message to author on June 2, 2004.

[16] Proverbs 8:1, 9, 11, 17, 20 (Good News Bible).

[17] Foster, *Streams*, 156.

[18] The following websites contain more information on Vanunu: www.vanunu.com and www.vanunu.org.

[19] Newell, *Creation*, xxiiii.

[20] Attwater, *Presence*, 17-18.

[21] Rilke, quoted in Wheatley, *Paying Attention*. www.womensworldinstitute.com/wheatley.html

[22] Strindberg, *Forgotten*, 2004.

[23] Matthew 5:9.

Printed in the United States
55549LVS00005BA/184-513

9 781425 953553